Rural Mission

A parish workbook for developing the mission of the rural church

Rural Mission

A parish workbook for developing the mission of the rural church

Leslie J Francis

and

Jeremy Martineau

with illustrations by
Chris Bishop

First published in September 2002

Acora Publishing
Arthur Rank Centre
Stoneleigh Park
Warwickshire CV8 2LZ

Cartoons by Chris Bishop
Cover Photo : Trevor Brown

ISBN 0 9540766 1 3

Typesetting by Acora Publishing,
Stoneleigh Park, Warwickshire CV8 2LZ

Printed by
Design & Print Services

Contents

Preface

This book is the fifth in a series which reflects the two authors' firm commitment to and clear confidence in the rural church. We are convinced that planning for the future of the rural church needs to be grounded in good empirical theology. This requires a combination of high quality research with local reflection and initiative.

Rural Mission is a parish workbook which invites local churches to undertake a thorough audit of their current context and provisions. The findings from the local audit can then be set alongside bench-marks established by a recent survey of rural churches across different parts of England. The workbook challenges local churches to use this information to stimulate new initiatives, growth and development.

We wish to record our gratitude to those who have assisted us in preparing this book. First, our gratitude goes to the Rural Officers in the dioceses which undertook the research for orchestrating the project and to the many clergy who gave time to completing the questionnaire. Without their help there could have been no book. Second, we are grateful to Chris Bishop for enlivening and enriching our words and figures with such entertaining and thought-provoking illustrations. Third, we record our gratitude to the Church of England Board of Mission for sponsoring the present analysis and to Mandy Robbins for undertaking that work on our behalf. Finally, we record our gratitude to Sallie Hughes who helped code the data, to Susan Thomas and Anna Halsall who helped shape the manuscript, and to Katrina Terrance who prepared the camera-ready copy.

Leslie J Francis
Centre for Studies in Rural Ministry
University of Wales, Bangor

Jeremy Martineau
Arthur Rank Centre
National Agricultural Centre

July 2002

Foreword

Reading this work-book is like walking through a Hall of Mirrors. It gives us the chance to take a long hard look at ourselves and from different angles. Some of us of course don't like looking in mirrors because we are worried about what we might see! And when we see the image we think that it must be distorted by an uneven mirror!

Jeremy Martineau and Leslie Francis have through their statistics and analysis given us a mirror on the rural church. The survey is fascinating. The skilful questions that follow help us to face up to the reality of life in rural communities and the role of the church.

Jeremy Martineau's wide experience as the Church of England's Rural Officer is brought to bear on the findings. As always his aim is to encourage and build-up the life of the Rural Church. If you've got this far I urge you to read on and look in the mirror! Whatever you see, look at with the faith that God loves us as we are and loves us too much to leave us where we are. The Spirit of Truth shows us the realities of what we are and promises us the adventure of something blown about by an unpredictable wind!

The Rt. Revd James Jones
Bishop of Liverpool
Chairman of the Board of Mission

July 2002

Audits and bench-marks

Rural Mission is a parish workbook designed to help rural churches to undertake a thorough audit of their current context and provisions. Rural churches are then invited to set the findings of their local audit against bench-marks established by a thorough survey of rural churches, the *Rural Churches Survey*.

The idea of these research-based bench-marks is to encourage local churches to assess their context and provision against the average reported by a number of churches within roughly the same size parishes. Bench-marking cannot tell you what you should be doing, but it helps you see how others are doing.

What does *Rural Mission* cover?

Rural Mission covers five key areas of relevance to the life of country churches in rural England and Wales and each area is explored by means of five topics.

The first area concerns the *services and ministry*. For many people it is the pattern of services and the ministry seen through conducting those services which act as the 'shop window' for the country church. Whether people attend that church or not, they tend to know that services are conducted there on some Sundays, if not all, and perhaps on some weekdays. They also tend to know who it is who is leading those services. The five key themes through which this area is explored are: the Sunday services, midweek services, the place of the vicar in today's rural community, the other people who lead services in the local church and the development of the notion of 'shared ministry'. What can be learned from conducting such an audit into services and ministry in your church?

The second area concerns the *local community*. A church which concentrates only on domestic issues like examining the Sunday services is clearly failing in its commitment to and mission to the whole community. Churches need to be actively aware of their environment and of their context. The issues which can be explored and which need to be explored in this area are endless. The authors of *Rural Mission* have decided to focus attention on five key themes. This section starts with two themes focusing on young people: what is the local provision for schools, and what voluntary provision exists for young people in terms of pre-school activities, activities for children and activities for teenagers. Young people are an important part of the rural community.

The third theme examines the local amenities, including public meeting places, shops and health care facilities. The last two themes examine the presence of other Christian denominations in the community, first in terms of their churches and chapels, and then in terms of participation in the life of the parish church. What can be learned by conducting such an audit into the local community serviced by rural churches?

The third area concerns *aspects of local church life*. The Church of England has passed through a phase of assessing church life in terms of the 'average Sunday attendance' and discovered that this measure is a very inadequate indicator of the strength of local churches. There are so many signs of life which are missed by focusing too much on this one indicator. It is nonetheless both important and salutary to consider such statistics. The five key themes through which this area is explored are as follows. First, attention has to be given to the main membership statistics, like the electoral roll, Easter and Christmas communicants and the usual Sunday attendance. Second, it is worth setting alongside the main membership statistics the numbers of people who attend the church on occasions like the Harvest Festival, the Remembrance Sunday service and the Christmas Carol service. These, too, are indicators of local church life. Third, attention is given to those major points of contact with life and death, through baptism and funerals. Further consideration is given to the presence of church groups, like the choir, the bellringers and the prayer and study groups. Finally questions are raised about parish 'away days' or weekends away. What can be learned by conducting such an audit into church life in your community?

The fourth area concerns the *church building*. The church building is crucial in so many ways. Not only is the church building a focus for the local Christian community, it often stands as a focal point of the rural community's identity and as a major point of interest for tourists and for visitors. The church building can be both a source of great pride and also a great drain on resources. The five key areas through which this area is explored are as follows. The section begins by examining the accessibility and security of the local church. Do churches really need to be kept locked? Then attention is drawn to the facilities offered by the local church, focusing on such matters as heating, lighting and toilets. The third theme charts the changes and improvements which have been made to the church over recent years. The final two themes explore ways in which the church building is currently used both for church-related activities and for community-related activities. What can be learned by conducting such an audit into your church building?

The fifth area concerns the idea of *every member ministry*. Clearly the changes which have taken place in the rural church over the past fifty years have rendered a traditional 'parson-centred' model of rural ministry untenable. A major emphasis in church strategy and teaching is now to promote the idea of every member ministry. This area is also explored by five key themes. The first four of the five themes follow a similar pattern and concentrate on different aspects of ministry: administration, education, pastoral care and liturgical ministry. The final theme takes a different perspective and examines ways in which members of the church permeate and influence the wider local community. What can be learned by conducting such an audit into the development of every member ministry within your church?

How is *Rural Mission* structured?

Each of the twenty-five sections has been shaped in the same way in order to facilitate a structured way of working through the material. There are six parts to each of these sections.

Take an audit

Each section begins by suggesting how a local audit could be conducted into the specific theme. Sometimes this may involve looking through church records. Sometimes this may involve going into the church or into the community to observe particular features. Sometimes this may involve talking with people and listening to them with care. Getting the evidence right is a crucial part to any audit.

Bench-marking

The second part invites you to place the findings from your local audit alongside the bench-mark statistics from the *Rural Churches Survey*. Over a thousand churches participated in this survey. The data have been presented from the survey according to community size. Four different sizes have been selected for this comparison:

communities under 200 people, communities with between 200 and 399 people, communities with between 400 and 899 people and communities with between 900 and 3,000 people.

Listening to the statistics

The third part offers some commentary on the statistics. Of course, in one sense, the statistics provide the raw data which each reader is invited to interpret in his or her own way. Statistics are properly open to a variety of interpretations and need to be used intelligently if they are to be of real benefit in assessing and shaping church policy. The two authors offer their own reflection on the statistics as one way of encouraging the readers to do their own reflection as well.

Talking points

The fourth part recognises that the local audit and the bench-marking statistics should together raise a number of issues for discussion and for debate. Here the two authors give voice to some of the issues which are raised in their own minds. Some readers may find this a helpful starting point for their own thinking and for stimulating group discussion. Other readers may prefer to start with their own questions.

Reflection

Each section continues with a reflection which focuses on a specific aspect of the theme.

Actions

Each section ends by inviting you to consider what actions should be taken as a consequence of this aspect of the audit.

How can *Rural Mission* be used?

Rural Mission has been designed as a workbook to encourage local churches to take stock of their context and of the provisions which they make within their context. The purpose of an audit is *not* to concentrate on where and how we are failing, but on what we can do better in the future. Faith that God provides the church with the resources needed for mission and for ministry should be sufficient to encourage us to go forward. So often the problem is *not* that God has failed to provide the resources, but that we have failed to recognise and to welcome what God has already provided.

As a workbook, *Rural Mission* can be used by individuals working on their own. However, *Rural Mission* has also been consciously designed for groups of people to work together in a church study group, a church working group or a church workshop.

When used by a group of people the first decision to be made concerns the number of sessions for which the group plans to meet. *Rural Mission* is able to provide resources for twenty-five sessions, but many churches will not wish to commit themselves to so many sessions working on one project and some will become bored if they were to decide to do so. While it is quite possible to tackle more than one theme in a session, the danger of doing this is that the group may be confronted with too much material at once and then experience difficulty in drawing any useful conclusions from the material which can lead to positive action points. Possibly a more productive way forward is for the group leader or for the Church Council to identify the most relevant aspects of the audit for the local situation and then to choose one or (at the most) two themes for each session.

How are groups best organised?

Groups may work best with between six and ten people. To cover such a wide range of view points will require experienced group leadership skills. The function of the group leader is to facilitate discussion, not to impose his or her own views. By modelling listening, the group leader will enable others to listen. It is important to allow space and time for sharing personal experiences which give rise to present opinions. The group leader will also need to be able to contain powerful and conflicting thoughts and emotions which may arise.

The aims of the local audit and of discussion on these themes is to increase the knowledge and awareness of those individuals who help to shape the mission of the rural church in a changing and developing environment. The group may include people of very different backgrounds, who bring with them very different experiences and very different expectations. It is particularly important that the established rural dwellers (who have known that local church all their lives) and the newcomers (who may have had their Christian faith shaped by a very different kind of church in suburbia or in the university town) are enabled to share experiences and perspectives. Each may have much to learn from the other. It is also important that those who have been Anglicans all their lives and those who have been shaped by other denominational traditions are enabled to share experiences and perspectives.

Generally, sessions should last for no more than one and a half hours. At the end of this time participants should be more aware of the origins and formation of their own views and those which others hold. They should have experienced difference as a positive contribution to life in the local church.

It is often helpful for refreshments to be served on arrival. The leader or host should ensure that each person is known to everyone. To invite each person to say why he or she has come may be a useful way of opening and introducing the subject.

It is often more creative to use the time in different ways: working in twos or fours, by brainstorming ideas which are written on the flip chart, by choosing to use silence for a time of reflection, and only using some of the time in plenary discussion. The audit itself may require the collection and organisation of specific pieces of information, including, for example, extracting data from the service registers or interviewing people who remember the history of the local church and community. It is so crucial to remember that the rural church cannot progress into the future without understanding, building on and integrating the past. Such tasks may well be divided among the group, and some may well need to be undertaken as preparation for the meeting, while others can be undertaken as part of the meeting.

Finally, it is important to recognise how much people differ from one another, and how different personality types react so very differently in groups. Extroverts, for example, will feel so much more at home with these group processes than introverts. It is important to allow introverts to contribute in their own way. Too much pressure to speak may force them to stay away.

How was the *Rural Churches Survey* conducted?

The *Rural Churches Survey* was conducted as partnership between Jeremy Martineau, the National Rural Officer of the Church of England, based at the Arthur Rank Centre, and Leslie J Francis, through the Centre for Ministry Studies, now based at the University of Wales, Bangor. The Church of England Rural Officers from six largely rural dioceses, representative of different geographical parts of England, took a key role in designing the survey and in handling the distribution to the churches within their area.

The notion of what counts as *rural* is quite elusive. When, for example, does a village grow to such a size that it has all the characteristics of a small town, rather than the characteristics more generally associated with rurality? From a pragmatic point of view, the *Rural Churches Survey* asked for data to be collected from all churches in rural communities with up to 3,000 inhabitants. A total of 956 churches within this size parameter responded to the survey, together with a further 94 churches from communities slightly over this threshold. For the purposes of the current presentation, churches above the threshold of 3,000 inhabitants are not included in the analysis.

Leslie J Francis' study, conducted in the early 1980s and published in his book *Rural Anglicanism* (1985) drew attention to the way in which the potential within rural churches was closely related to the size of the community in which they were located. He interpreted his finding in terms of certain thresholds and saturation points. For example, a church in a very small community may command a high level of support from the key members, since they would be clearly missed if they began to reduce their level of support. At the same time, however, such small churches are unlikely to have the resources to operate such features as a church choir, which might be capable of drawing in fringe members. After a certain threshold has been passed the local community is large enough to support a church choir, say, and the choir grows to a certain point where saturation is reached. At saturation point, the members become content with their own membership and, consciously or unconsciously, cease to try to draw in new members.

Much more research is needed to understand properly the dynamics of rural church life within different sizes of community. For bench-marking purposes, however, four different sizes of community have been identified. The first group of churches are those located in communities of fewer than 200 people. There were 260 communities of this size in the database. The second group of churches are those located in communities of between 200 and 399 inhabitants. There were 246 communities of this size in the database. The third group of churches are those located in communities of between 400 and 899 inhabitants. There were 218 communities of this size in the database. The fourth group of churches are those located in communities of between 900 and 3,000 inhabitants. There were 232 communities of this size in the database. By making the divisions in community size at this point, all four groups of churches were represented by roughly comparable numbers.

When referring to the bench-marking statistics, you are invited first to see how your own local audit shapes up against other churches within the same category of community size, and then to reflect on how churches in larger or smaller communities generally shape up by way of comparison.

PART ONE

Services and Ministry

1 Sunday services

Take an audit

Go back through the church register of services. Ignore the figures concerned with the number of people who attended or who received communion. Just look at the *pattern* of services week by week.

Draw up the pattern of services for a typical month.

- What happens on the first, second, third, fourth and fifth Sunday of the month?
- What types of services are held?
- At what times are the services held?

Find out for how long has this pattern of services been in place.

- When were changes last made?
- Who decided on the pattern?
- Who was consulted about the pattern?
- Why was this pattern chosen?
- Who used to attend church, but does so no longer? Why is this so?

Look back through the registers to see what happened in the past.

- What was the pattern in 1990?
- What was the pattern in 1980?
- What was the pattern in 1970?
- What was the pattern in 1960?
- What was the pattern in 1950?
- What has caused the changes to take place?

Bench-marking

The *Rural Churches Survey* provided a pattern of services for each Sunday of the month. Overall the number of services remained quite constant on the first, second, third and fourth Sundays of the month, although often the services were happening in different churches. Overall fewer services took place on the fifth Sunday of the month when shared worship or benefice services are arranged.

Here are the bench-marking statistics for the first Sunday of the month according to community size.

Table 1: Number of services on the first Sunday of the month by community size.

number of services	under 200 %	200-399 %	400-899 %	900 plus %
none	37	10	7	4
one	61	82	69	40
two	2	7	19	38
three	0	1	4	19

Listening to the statistics

- On a typical Sunday in two out of every five communities (37%) of under 200 people there is no service held in the local church.
- On a typical Sunday in one out of every ten communities (10%) of between 200 and 399 people there is no service held in the local church.
- In communities of under 400 people the norm is for a maximum of one service to be held in the local church on a typical Sunday.
- Nearly one in every four communities (23%) of between 400 and 899 people have at least two services on a typical Sunday.
- Nearly three in every five communities (57%) of 900 or more people have at least two services on a typical Sunday and one in every five (19%) have three services.

Talking points

- Does the current pattern of Sunday services reflect the needs of the community?
- Is it better to stick to the same time every Sunday or to have different times on different Sundays?
- How easy is it for visitors and for occasional attenders to know when services take place?
- Would it be possible and desirable to have a service at the same time every Sunday and could lay people lead some of these services?
- Are there particular sectors of the community who are better served than other sectors by the current pattern of services?

Reflection

In many ways the Sunday services provide a main 'shop window' into the life of the rural church. These services are important to the regular churchgoers. Yet they also need to be accessible to the local inhabitants who only wish to attend church from time to time. They also need to be accessible to visitors and to those who come to the countryside for holidays, for rest, for recreation and for refreshment. Are the services in your church really 'public' services or have they been captured to feel more like a 'private' club?

Actions

What actions would you want to recommend as a result of your audit on Sunday services?

2 Midweek services

Take an audit

Take another look at the church register of services. This time ignore the Sunday services and see what you can learn about midweek services during an ordinary month.

- Is there currently a pattern of midweek communion services?
- Is there currently a pattern of daily offices (morning prayer and evening prayer) being said in the church?
- Was there a time when there was a different pattern?
- When did the pattern last change, and why?

Examine the registers to see if there are particular times of the year when special midweek services take place.

- Is there a service on Ash Wednesday?
- Is there a service on Maundy Thursday and Good Friday?
- Are midweek services held during Lent?
- Is there a service on Ascension Day?
- Is there a midweek service for the Patronal Festival?
- Is there a midweek Harvest Festival?

Bench-marking

The *Rural Churches Survey* asked two separate questions regarding the frequency of midweek communion services and regarding the frequency of the daily offices (morning prayer and evening prayer) being said in the church. Here are the bench-marking statistics according to community size.

Table 2: Frequency of midweek services by community size.

	under 200 %	200-399 %	400-899 %	900 plus %
communion				
weekly	4	8	22	40
monthly	2	4	6	9
sometimes	27	42	45	37
never	67	46	27	14
morning/evening prayer				
daily	3	8	16	29
weekly	4	12	13	16
sometimes	19	24	28	21
never	74	56	43	34

Listening to the statistics

- Rural churches are more likely to make provision for midweek communion services than for the daily offices of morning prayer and evening prayer. Overall 53% of rural churches never have the daily offices and 41% never have midweek communion services.
- A midweek communion service is never held in two-thirds (67%) of churches in communities of under 200 people.
- A midweek communion service is never held in a half (48%) of churches in communities of between 200 and 399 people.
- A midweek communion service is never held in a quarter (28%) of churches in communities of between 400 and 899 people.
- A midweek communion service is never held in one in every seven (15%) of churches in communities of 900 or more people.
- Morning or evening prayer is held on a daily basis in more than a quarter (29%) of churches in communities of 900 or more people.

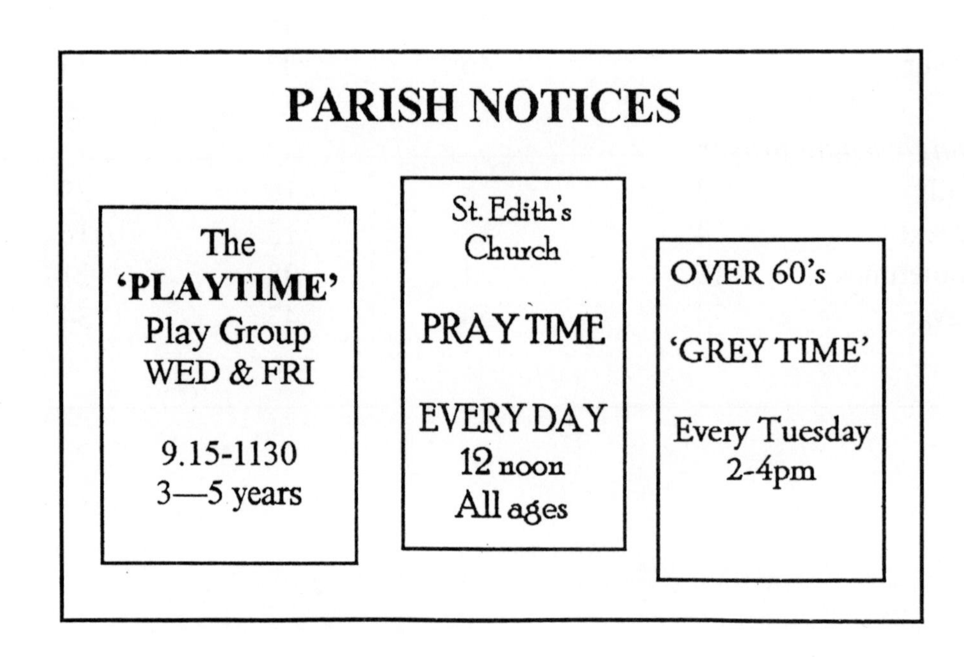

Talking points

- Is the present pattern of midweek services the right one for your church?
- Is there a point to midweek services even if only one or two people come?
- Are there people in your church who use a daily or regular pattern of prayer in their own homes?
- Are there people who would be willing to organise and lead a midweek service in your church?
- Does your vicar use any of the churches in his/her care for daily offices?
- Are there times in the year when it would be appropriate for your church to hold additional midweek communion services?

Reflection

There are two different but important rationales for rural churches holding midweek services, including communion, morning prayer and evening prayer. First there is benefit for the people who come out to pray. If there are people who take a prayer life seriously and their working constraints permit them to make time available, a regular commitment to meeting with others for prayer can be a real source of encouragement and strength. Second, there is benefit for the wider community. Churches which are used regularly for services and for prayer act as a living witness to a living faith. Churches which remain unused and empty (and locked) stand merely as museums to a past age and to a lost faith.

Actions

What actions would you want to recommend as a result of your audit on midweek services?

3 Vicar

Take an audit

Begin by looking in the church to see if there is a list of previous vicars.

- How far back can you trace the vicars for your church?
- How long have the vicars usually stayed in your church?
- How old have some of the vicars been in the past when they retired?
- How many churches was your vicar responsible for in 1980, in 1960, in 1930 and in 1900?

Does your vicar today live in the parish? If not:

- How far back do you have to go to a time when a vicar last lived in the parish?
- Is there an old vicarage or an old rectory in the parish?
- When was it sold?
- How was the decision reached regarding where the vicar should live?

How old is your vicar today? Has your vicar yet reached the age of sixty?

Is your church part of a multi-parish care? If so:

- For how many churches is your vicar responsible?
- How long has this been the case?
- When did the size of the benefice last change and why?

Bench-marking

The *Rural Churches Survey* asked three key and interesting questions about the current incumbents serving rural churches. These questions were:

- Does the vicar live in the parish?
- How old is the vicar?
- For how many churches does the vicar have care?

These three questions generated a lot of information. For the bench-marking statistics cited in table 3, only the most useful data are presented. Previous research has shown that a higher proportion of clergy in their sixties seem to be deployed in small parishes. The figures, therefore, concentrate on the proportions of clergy aged sixty or over in the different sizes of community. Clergy with care of five or more churches need to think of their ministry in radically different ways. Clearly, for example, they are no longer able to take one service in each church every Sunday. The figures, therefore, concentrate on the proportions of churches in different sizes of community which share their priest with a total of at least five churches.

Table 3: The vicar by community size.

	under 200 %	200-399 %	400-899 %	900 plus %
lives in the parish	14	24	45	69
is aged 60 or over	37	33	28	31
has care of 5 or more churches	36	27	17	8

Listening to the statistics

- The larger the parish, the more likely the vicar is to live there. Only 14% of parishes with under 200 people have a resident vicar. The proportions then rise to 24% in parishes of 200-399 people, to 45% in parishes of 400-899 people, and to 69% in parishes of 900 or more people.
- The smaller the parish, the more likely it is to share the vicar with a greater

number of other churches. Only 8% of the parishes with 900 or more people are part of benefices of five or more churches. The proportion rises to 17% for parishes with 400-899 people, to 27% for parishes with 200-399 people, and to 36% for parishes with under 200 people.

- Small parishes are more likely to be served by a vicar aged 60 or over. Thus, 37% of vicars in parishes of under 200 are in their sixties, compared with 31% of vicars in larger parishes.
- The small parishes of under 200 people are least likely to have a resident vicar, most likely to be part of a benefice of at least five churches, and most likely to be served by a vicar aged 60 or over.

"Welcome to this Seminar on Rural Ministry. There are three areas to be addressed. Getting to grips with Rural Issues, organising patterns of Worship, and a practical session in Rally Driving."

Talking points

- What are the advantages of having the vicar living in the parish?
- What are the disadvantages of having the vicar living in the parish?

- What are the strengths which can be brought to ministry by clergy in their sixties?
- What are the disadvantages of rural clergy being in their sixties?
- Is ministry organised differently in benefices of five or more churches?
- What is different in ministry for clergy who have responsibility for five or more churches?
- Are small parishes better served by being joined to one or two larger parishes, or by being joined with five or six other small parishes?
- Is the *minster model*, where clergy serve rural areas from the main town, worth considering?

Reflection

Rural ministry has changed a great deal in the last fifty years. As costs of ministry have escalated rural rectories have been sold and rural churches have been amalgamated into multi-parish benefices. In more recent years some dioceses have taken the bold step of keeping the rural vicarage and deploying from it a recently retired priest (who requires no stipend) or a non-stipendiary priest who is supported by secular employment. This is a vision which needed fostering twenty years earlier.

Tradition suggests that older clergy have always been attracted to small country parishes. Recent research has shown, however, that the changing shape of rural ministry may render this practice inappropriate.

Actions

What actions would you want to recommend as a result of your audit on the local stipendiary ministry provision? *Rural Ministry* (published by ACORA in 2000) explores the attitudes of lay Anglicans to some of these questions.

4 Other officiants

Take an audit

What proportions of the services in your church are conducted by the vicar? When the vicar is not present, who is it who takes the service?

- Who are the retired clergy who assist in your church?
- Who are the licensed readers who assist in your church?
- Who are the lay people properly authorised to take services in the vicar's absence?
- Who are the lay people who take services in the vicar's absence, but without formal authorisation, say from the bishop?
- Are there other stipendiary clergy who come to take services in the vicar's absence?
- Are there non-stipendiary clergy who come to take services in the vicar's absence?

When it is especially difficult to find people to conduct the services in your church?

Look back through the service registers in your church and note who has been responsible for conducting services at different periods in the past.

- Is today's pattern significantly different from what it used to be?
- If today's pattern is significantly different from what it used to be, when did things begin to change, and why?

Bench-marking

The *Rural Churches Survey* compiled a great deal of information on who conducts the services when the vicar is not there. This includes occasions when the vicar is off sick and when the vicar is away on holiday. This also includes those occasions when the vicar is busy taking services within another church within the benefice. Given the current shape of rural ministry, neither the vicar nor the vicar's stipendiary colleagues now have the capacity for taking all the services which are either required or take place.

Here are the bench-marking statistics which show the proportions of rural churches within different community sizes which benefited from services taken by six different categories of minister in the vicar's absence within a twelve month period.

Table 4: Proportions of churches which have had at least one service taken in the last twelve months in the vicar's absence by different categories of minister by community size.

	under 200 %	200-399 %	400-899 %	900 plus %
retired clergy	50	60	67	73
readers	50	63	57	61
other stipendiary clergy	24	29	29	32
non-stipendiary clergy	9	12	13	15
authorised lay people	7	10	12	14
unauthorised lay people	6	12	17	13

Listening to the statistics

- It is the retired clergy who are most in evidence taking services in rural churches. Across all four community sizes, 62% of churches have experienced retired clergy taking services in the vicar's absence over a twelve month period.
- Next to the retired clergy, it is the licensed readers who are most in evidence taking services in rural churches. Across the four community sizes, 57% of churches

have experienced licensed readers taking services in the vicar's absence over a twelve month period.

- Other stipendiary clergy continue to play an important role in taking services in rural churches in the vicar's absence. Across the four community sizes, 28% of churches have experienced other stipendiary clergy taking services in the vicar's absence over a twelve month period.
- By way of comparison, authorised and unauthorised lay people are responsible for taking services in only 11% and 12% of churches respectively across all four community sizes. Moreover, the larger the community, the more likely it is that lay people are available to take the services in the vicar's absence.
- Comparatively few rural churches (12% over the four community sizes) find services taken by non-stipendiary clergy in the vicar's absence. Moreover, the larger communities are more likely to be able to call out vocations to non-stipendiary clergy, in comparison with the smaller communities.

'Yes, we are very rural, but we are helped by retired clergy who are able to travel long distances thanks to our satellite navigation system'

Talking points

- What contribution do retired clergy make to ministry in your church?
- Do retired clergy enjoy coming to take services in your church?

- Is it right that rural churches should rely so heavily on retired clergy?
- How does the congregation feel about retired clergy taking the services?
- How pressed are the stipendiary clergy in your area (deanery) to offer cover when their colleagues (like your vicar) are off sick or on holiday?
- Are we wise to rely on clergy to take so many of the services?
- What is the potential for developing lay ministry to provide services when the vicar is away or taking services in other churches?
- What are the benefits of developing local ministry teams?
- What kind of people become non-stipendiary clergy in your area?

Reflection

There are now more retired clergy in the Church of England than parochial stipendiary clergy. Many seem to retire to rural areas and offer a crucial service to the rural church. Because it is wiser to retire to the larger rural communities (where there are shops and better access to medical facilities) it is the small market town which is more likely to benefit from resident retired clergy than the smaller villages. Retired clergy are often very conscious of 'stepping on the toes' of their local vicar and will often patiently wait to be invited to share in ministry in the parish. There are now also more readers than parochial stipendiary clergy.

Actions

What actions would you want to recommend as a result of your audit of other officiants who take services in the vicar's absence?

5 Shared ministry

Take an audit

What proportions of services in your church are conducted by the vicar? When the vicar *is* present, does the vicar tend to take sole charge of leading the service, or does the vicar share leadership with others?

- Who are the retired clergy who assist in services when the vicar is there?
- Who are the licensed readers who assist in services when the vicar is there?
- Who are the lay people (authorised or unauthorised) who assist in services when the vicar is there?
- Who are the clergy (stipendiary or non-stipendiary) who assist in services when the vicar is there?
- Does your vicar ever attend services in your church as a member of congregation, while other people conduct the service?

Has the level of shared ministry in the conduct of services changed at all in recent years?

- If so, when did the change take place, and why?
- Who decides who is going to assist in the conduct of services?

Look through the service registers and discover whether those who assist the vicar in conducting services are always invited to sign the service register.

Bench-marking

The *Rural Churches Survey* compiled a great deal of information on who shares in the conduct of services when the vicar is present. Generally this means that the vicar is present for the whole service, but someone else preaches the sermon, leads the intercessions, or leads part of the service. Sometimes in the rural church, it means that the vicar will leave one service before it is finished in order to drive to another church to pick up leadership of a service someone else has already started.

Here are the bench-marking statistics which show the proportions of rural churches within different community sizes which benefited from the vicar sharing leadership of worship with six different categories of minister within a twelve month period.

Table 5: Proportions of churches in which the vicar has shared the leadership of services at least once in the last twelve months with different categories of minister by community size.

	under 200 %	200-399 %	400-899 %	900 plus %
retired clergy	18	14	25	31
readers	38	43	46	53
other stipendiary clergy	18	18	21	24
non-stipendiary clergy	6	5	8	9
authorised lay people	11	17	24	31
unauthorised lay people	7	12	16	19

Listening to the statistics

- It is the licensed readers who are most in evidence taking services alongside the vicar. Across all four community sizes, 45% of churches have experienced licensed readers taking services alongside the vicar over a twelve month period.
- Next to licensed readers, it is the retired clergy who are most in evidence taking services alongside the vicar. Across all four community sizes, 22% of churches have experienced retired clergy taking services alongside the vicar over a twelve month period.

- Stipendiary colleagues have shared leadership with the vicar in 20% of churches across the community sizes during a twelve month period. Often this may be a special occasion when the vicar invites a stipendiary colleague to preach, like, for example, the Harvest Festival.
- The statistics make it clear that shared ministry with readers has taken greater hold in the larger communities. For example, while readers have assisted the vicar during a twelve month period in conducting services in 38% of churches in communities of under 200 inhabitants, the proportion rises to 53% in communities of 900 or more inhabitants.
- Authorised lay people are involved in sharing leadership of services with the vicar in only 20% of the churches across the community sizes.
- The statistics make it clear that shared ministry with authorised lay people has taken greater hold in the larger communities. For example, while authorised lay people have assisted the vicar during a twelve month period in conducting services in 11% of churches in communities of under 200 inhabitants, the proportion rises to 31% in communities of over 900 inhabitants.

'Thanks to the use of a digital hymnal, power point projection, pre-recorded homilies, subtle use of lighting and a couple of well positioned cardboard cut outs of the Vicar and Organist, our weekly service now comes in a suitcase'

Talking points

- Is it helpful for the congregation to see that the leadership of services is shared by the vicar with others?
- Is it helpful for the vicar to share leadership of services with others?

- Who is trained and authorised in your church to assist the vicar in the leadership of services?
- Are there other people in your church who may wish or may be willing to train and to become authorised to share leadership of the services with the vicar?
- When lay people are authorised to assist the vicar in leadership of services, should they be encouraged to do so throughout the whole benefice?

Reflection

The conduct of services and preaching are both skilled liturgical functions for which it is appropriate to submit to a selection process, to undertake proper training and to receive formal recognition or licensing. Shared ministry is not simply an expedient way of keeping the church running with fewer clergy. Shared ministry is a response to the profound theological principle that all the people of God are called and equipped for ministry with differing skills, gifts and aptitudes.

A church which wishes to equip the people of God better to fulfil their ministry of leadership in the vicar's absence, would be wise to begin to encourage people to explore their gifts for ministry by working alongside the vicar when the vicar is present. Shared ministry is a proper response to God's call to the laity and a proper solution to the changing demands made on rural clergy.

Actions

What actions would you want to recommend as a result of your audit of the practice and opportunities for shared ministry in your church? Draw on diocesan resources and consult with appropriate diocesan staff in exploring this issue.

PART TWO

Local Community

6 Schools

Take an audit

Make a thorough estimate of the number of children and young people of school age who live in your community. Estimate the number of children of primary school age and of secondary school age.

Then draw up a map of where the children of primary school age go to school.

- Is there a primary school in the community?
- If not, how far do the children have to travel to their primary school?
- If children travel from the community to attend primary school elsewhere, do they all travel to the same school?
- If they travel by school bus, for how long are they away from home each day?

Draw up a map of where the children of secondary school age go to school.

- How far do they have to travel?
- What time does the school bus pick them up and return them home?

If there is a primary school in the community, is it a Church of England voluntary aided or voluntary controlled school?

- When was the school first opened in the community?

If there is no primary school in the community, did there used to be one?

- When was the school built?
- Who built it?
- When was the school closed?
- Why was it closed?

Bench-marking

The *Rural Churches Survey* mapped which churches were in communities which supported primary, middle and secondary schools. While most rural education follows the traditional two tier pattern of primary and secondary schools, some developed the three tier system of first, middle and upper schools. The development of the three tier system made it more difficult for some villages to retain their village school which forfeited two year groups of pupils. On the other hand, some small market towns, which could never had maintained a secondary school, were able to support a middle school.

Here are the bench-marking statistics for primary, middle and secondary schools according to community size. In this table primary schools are classified as voluntary aided, voluntary controlled and non-denominational.

Table 6: Proportion of communities supporting schools by community size.

	under 200 %	200-399 %	400-899 %	900 plus %
middle or secondary	0	0	3	13
primary voluntary aided	2	7	16	18
primary voluntary controlled	3	21	33	35
primary non-denominational	4	10	23	37

Listening to the statistics

- Only a small proportion of communities with between 400 and 899 inhabitants support a post-primary school (3%). The proportion rises only to 13% in communities with between 900 and 3,000 inhabitants.
- Only one in ten (9%) of communities with less than 200 inhabitants support a primary school. The proportion rises to 38% of communities with between 200 and 399 inhabitants.
- The majority of communities with more than 400 inhabitants support a primary school. This is the case for 72% of communities between 400 and 900 inhabitants

and for 90% of communities with 900 or more inhabitants.

- Throughout the rural communities Church of England schools are twice as common as non-denominational schools. While 18% of rural communities under 3,000 inhabitants support a non-denominational school, 33% of these communities support a Church of England voluntary school.
- Where the local primary school is a Church of England school, this school is twice as likely to be voluntary controlled as to be voluntary aided.

'It's a good Primary School - pity about the journey - but he's got used to taking breakfast, lunch and supper with him'

Talking points

- What benefits does a village school bring to a community?
- What are the real differences between a non-denominational school, a church voluntary aided school and a church voluntary controlled school?
- What links exist between your church and the nearest primary school? Could these links be further strengthened?
- What benefits does a village school have for the children who attend it?
- What disadvantages does a village school have for the children who attend it?
- What disadvantages do young children experience when they have to be taken out of their community to attend primary school?

Reflection

The Church of England was a great pioneer in the provision of education for the nation's children following the founding of the National Society in 1811. At the time of the 1944 Education Act church schools had the option between choosing aided and controlled status. For aided status the church had to continue to invest in the building, but retained rights over appointing the majority of the managers and over religious education. For controlled status the church was freed from on-going financial liability but lost the right to determine the religious education syllabus and could appoint only a minority of governors. The strong presence of church schools in rural communities witnesses to these pioneering efforts in the past.

Actions

What actions would you want to recommend as a result of your audit on schooling?

7 Provision for the young

Take an audit

Undertake a thorough survey of the provisions which exist for children and young people of different ages in your community.

What exists for pre-school children in your community, for example, in terms of parent and toddler groups, play schools and other activities?

- What is provided by your church?
- What is provided by other Christian groups?
- What is provided by secular groups?

What exists for the children of primary school age in your community, for example, in terms of after school clubs, holiday clubs, weekend sporting activities and uniformed groups?

- What is provided by your church?
- What is provided by other Christian groups?
- What is provided by secular groups?

What exists for the children of secondary school age in your community, for example, in terms of social and recreational activities?

- What is provided by your church?
- What is provided by other Christian groups?
- What is provided by secular groups?

Bench-marking

The *Rural Churches Survey* mapped the provisions made for children of different ages and the bodies which offered those provisions. Here are the bench-marking statistics for pre-school children, for the under 12s, and for the 12s plus according to community size. In this table the providers are classified within three categories: secular, Anglican or Church of England and other denominations.

Table 7: Proportions of communities supporting provisions for children and young people according to sponsorship by community size.

	under 200 %	200-399 %	400-899 %	900 plus %
group for pre-school children				
secular	20	42	61	76
Anglican	4	3	9	11
other denominations	1	1	1	2
group for under 12s				
secular	4	13	24	27
Anglican	13	22	32	39
other denominations	2	4	6	10
group for 12s plus				
secular	5	19	26	33
Anglican	8	11	18	26
other denominations	1	2	5	6

Listening to the statistics

- The age group best provided for are the pre-schoolers. The age group least well provided for are the 12s plus. When all four community sizes are considered together, 57% support provision for pre-schoolers, 48% support provision for the under 12s, and 39% support provision for the 12s plus.

- The Church of England makes comparatively little provision for pre-schoolers. While overall 49% of communities under 3,000 inhabitants have secular groups for pre-schoolers, only 7% have groups sponsored by the Church of England, and 1% have groups sponsored by other Christian denominations.
- Taken together the churches make twice as much contribution to work with the under 12s compared with secular groups. While overall 16% of communities under 3,000 inhabitants have secular groups for under 12s, 26% have groups sponsored by the Church of England, and a further 5% have groups sponsored by other Christian denominations.
- Taken together the churches sponsor as much work among the 12s plus as is sponsored by secular groups. Overall 20% of communities under 3,000 inhabitants have secular groups for 12s plus. At the same time 16% of these communities have groups for 12s plus sponsored by the Church of England, and a further 3% have groups sponsored by other Christian denominations.
- Provisions for all three age groups increase in step with community size.

'It's the Vicar's idea—and I have an 'orrible idea it won't work'

Talking points

- What more could your church be doing for the pre-schoolers?
- What more could your church be doing for the under 12s?
- What more could your church be doing for the 12s plus?
- What do the under 12s do in your community in their spare time?
- What do the 12s plus do in your community in their spare time?
- How easy is it for teenagers in your community to stay on at school for after school clubs, given the schedule of the school bus?
- How accessible are the sports and leisure facilities in your area to teenagers living in your community?

Reflection

Parents with pre-school children living in small villages may experience the same needs for help with their children as parents living in larger communities. The under 12s living in small villages may want and need activities to encourage their attention as much as children living in larger communities. Teenagers living in small villages may need as much opportunity to engage in social, recreational, leisure and sporting activities as teenagers living in larger communities. In every case, the data say that there are fewer opportunities open to them in the smaller places. Further resources to help reflection on the church's work among teenagers is provided in *Rural Youth* (published by ACORA in 2001). This book is based on a large survey among 13-15 year olds about their attitudes to life's big questions.

Actions

What actions would you want to recommend as a result of your audit on provisions for the young?

8 Amenities

Take an audit

Take a close look at your community and examine the amenities which it provides. Draw a rough map of the community and locate these amenities on the map.

What does the community support as places where people can meet?

- Is there a church hall?
- Is there a village hall?
- Is there a public house or inn?
- Is there a children's play area?

What resources does the community provide to support the elderly and families without transport?

- Is there a general store?
- Is there a post office?
- Is there a doctor's surgery?

What other public amenities are there in the community?

- Is there a public pay phone?
- Is there a public convenience?
- Are there seats in suitable places?

If these amenities are not available in the community, how far do people have to travel?

- How far away is the nearest post office?
- How far away is the nearest general store?
- How far away is the nearest doctor's surgery?
- How far away is the nearest pharmacy?

Bench-marking

The *Rural Churches Survey* recorded the presence in each community of the following specified amenities: church hall, village hall, public house or inn, children's play area, general store, post office, doctor's surgery, public pay phone and public convenience. Here are the bench-marking statistics for these nine specified amenities according to community size.

Table 8: Proportion of communities supporting specified amenities by community size.

	under 200 %	200-399 %	400-899 %	900 plus %
public pay phone	71	92	95	95
public house/inn	40	81	93	94
village hall	41	71	85	82
post office	29	50	77	87
general store	14	34	68	84
children's play area	8	29	48	69
church hall	8	12	17	32
public convenience	4	7	11	16
doctor's surgery	1	7	18	41

Listening to the statistics

- Each of the specified amenities followed the same pattern of being least available in the smaller communities and of being most available in the larger communities.
- Only 40% of communities with under 200 people have a public house, but the proportion rises to 94% in communities with 900 or more people.
- Only 29% of communities with under 200 people have a post office, but the proportion rises to 87% in communities with 900 or more people.
- Only 14% of communities with under 200 people have a general store, but the proportion rises to 84% in communities with 900 or more people.
- Only 1% of communities with under 200 people have a doctor's surgery, but the

proportion rises to 41% in communities with 900 or more people.

- Small communities of under 200 people are four times more likely to have a village hall (41%) than to have a church hall (8%).

The Village of Little Doze were grateful for the daily delivery of letters and parcels, but the milk delivery still had to be perfected.

Talking points

- Is a church hall a liability or an asset?
- Is all the work involved in keeping a village hall worth it?
- How can the church also function as a community meeting place?
- Who loses out when the village loses its post office?
- What can be done to make village shops viable?
- Is there somewhere in the community where doctors could hold a surgery?
- What does the public house or inn offer to the community?
- Is there still a need for public pay phones when so many people own mobiles?

Reflection

The idea that the rural community is the place where people work, live, and share a common life is almost vanished. Rural communities are often places from which people commute to work, places where the retired settle escaping from the towns, places where people have second homes and holiday lets. Building community in such places can take a lot of effort. Where the parsonage still exists and where the parson regards the house as a key tool in ministry, the parsonage can become a key meeting place. Villages without parsonages, without village halls, and without a village pub can struggle to find places to meet and a common ground on which the different sections of the community can come together.

Actions

What actions would you want to recommend as a result of your audit of the amenities in your community?

9 Other churches

Take an audit

Look round the community for other churches and chapels currently in use.

- Which denominations have churches or chapels in the community?
- What services are held by these denominations?
- What is the membership and attendance?
- Is there a House Church/New Church meeting in the community?

Look round the community for signs of other churches and chapels no longer in current use.

- Which denominations built these churches and chapels?
- When were they closed?
- Why were they closed?
- What are they used for now?

Work out how far people will have to travel from your community to find different churches and chapels.

- How far away is the nearest Baptist church?
- How far away is the nearest Methodist church?
- How far away is the nearest Roman Catholic church?
- How far away is the nearest Salvation Army Citadel?
- How far away is the nearest United Reformed church?

Note where there are ministers of other denominations resident in the community.
Note whether other denominations ever hold services in the parish church.

Bench-marking

The *Rural Churches Survey* mapped which churches were in communities which supported other churches and chapels. The three denominations most frequently mentioned were Methodist, Roman Catholic and Baptist. For this reason the bench-marking statistics have separated out these three denominations for individual reference. The *Rural Churches Survey* also noted if there were ministers from other denominations resident in the community, and if other denominations held regular services in the parish church.

Here are the bench-marking statistics for the presence of other denominations by community size. In this table the presence of other denominations is explored in three ways: churches or chapels currently in use, resident ministers and services held in the parish church.

Table 9: Presence of other denominations by community size.

	under 200 %	200-399 %	400-899 %	900 plus %
Methodist	15	29	47	53
Roman Catholic	3	2	7	10
Baptist	1	2	5	8
Other	1	3	10	14
Other denominations hold services in parish church	3	4	5	7
Other resident minister	4	2	6	14

Listening to the statistics

- Next to the Church of England the strongest denominational presence in rural communities is that of the Methodist Church. Across all four community sizes there is one Methodist chapel for every three parish churches: 35% of the communities have a Methodist chapel.

- A long way behind the Methodists come the Roman Catholics and the Baptists. Across all four community sizes, 5% have a Roman Catholic church and 4% have a Baptist chapel.
- Very few rural communities have a resident minister from another denomination. Across all four community sizes just 7% have a non-Anglican resident minister.
- Very few parish churches are used by other denominations for holding their services. Across all four community sizes, just 5% of parish churches are used in this way.
- The likelihood of other denominations being active in rural communities is very clearly related to community size. This is demonstrated by Methodism which retains chapels in 15% of communities under 200, 29% of communities between 200 and 399, 47% of communities between 400 and 899, and 53% of communities of 900 or over.

One of the poor 'stretched' Anglican clergy that reports talk about.

Talking points

- In today's society does anything make the services and teaching of the denominations really distinctive?

- Does the provision of more than one church or chapel in a rural community strengthen the overall Christian witness?
- Can we continue to afford separate buildings and ministries?
- What does the denominational structure of the churches today say to the unchurched majority in society?
- Could more use be made of the parish church by other denominations?
- Why are members of some denominations apparently so willing to travel a distance to their own church or chapel, but Anglicans remain reluctant to attend services in the church in the next village?

Reflection

Unlike any other denomination the Church of England has remained committed to supporting a church in as many rural communities as possible, although there is also a slow but steady closure of rural Anglican churches when the congregation becomes too few and when the building becomes too costly to repair.

Currently several denominations maintain an increasingly stretched staff of clergy to serve the same geographical area and to keep competing buildings in repair. Any coherent strategy for rural ministry in the future needs to be undertaken on the basis of inter-denominational co-operation, mutual recognition of ministries, and a planned rationalisation of buildings.

Actions

What actions would you want to recommend as a result of your audit on other churches?

10 Ecumenism

Take an audit

Look round your church congregation and church membership. Discover how many people worshipping with you today had their personal or their family roots in another denomination.

- Do you have Methodists in your church congregation?
- Do you have Baptists in your church congregation?
- Do you have Roman Catholics in your church congregation?
- Do you have Presbyterians/United Reformed Church members in your church congregation?
- Do you have members of the Salvation Army in your church congregation?
- Do you have members of other denominations in your church congregation?

Then examine how much your usual Sunday worship recognises and reflects the presence of people shaped by other denominational traditions.

- What is there that might remind people of their Methodist background?
- What is there that might remind people of their Baptist background?
- What is there that might remind people of their Roman Catholic background?

Consider how much your church recognises and welcomes the participation of ministers from other denominations.

- When did a Methodist minister or Methodist local preacher last preach in your church?
- When did a Roman Catholic priest last lead worship in your church?

Bench-marking

The *Rural Churches Survey* mapped the proportions of churches which were conscious of having people brought up in or shaped by other denominational traditions worship with them on a regular basis. The four denominations most frequently mentioned were Methodist, Roman Catholic, Baptist, and Presbyterian or United Reformed Church. For this reason the bench-marking statistics have separated out these four denominations for individual reference.

Here are the bench-marking statistics for the ecumenical nature of Anglican congregations. This table shows the proportions of Anglican churches in different sizes of community which recognise in their regular congregations Methodists, Baptists, Roman Catholics and Presbyterians or members of the United Reformed Church (URC).

Table 10: Ecumenical presence in congregations in the Anglican churches by community size.

	under 200 %	200-399 %	400-899 %	900 plus %
Methodists	42	41	56	52
Roman Catholics	15	21	28	29
Presbyterians/URC members	4	7	11	14
Baptists	4	4	11	14

Listening to the statistics

- In practice rural Anglican congregations have become ecumenical bodies. Taking all four community sizes together, nearly half (47%) of Anglican congregations contain Methodists and nearly a quarter (23%) contain Roman Catholics.
- Across all four community sizes nearly one in ten Anglican congregations contain Presbyterians/URC members (9%) or Baptists (8%).
- Churches in the smallest communities (under 200) are almost as likely to have Methodists in the congregation as churches in the largest communities (900 plus). The proportion increases from 42% to 52%.

- Churches in the largest communities (900 plus) are twice as likely to have Roman Catholics in the congregation as churches in the smallest communities (under 200). The proportion decreases from 29% to 15%.
- Churches in the largest communities (900 plus) are between three and four times as likely to have Baptists or Presbyterians/URC members in the congregations as churches in the smallest communities (under 200). The proportion decreases from 14% to 4%.

'I don't think he's got that quite right!'

Talking points

- How could the services in your church affirm Methodists who choose to worship with you?
- How could the services in your church affirm Roman Catholics who choose to worship with you?

- How could the services in your church affirm Baptists who choose to worship with you?
- Are there Methodist ministers, Methodist local preachers or Roman Catholic priests who would welcome being invited to lead services in your church?
- Are there leaders from other Christian denominations living in your community who would welcome the invitation to share in leadership of worship in your church?
- Has your congregation ever made an official visit to join in worship of another denomination?

Reflection

All the denominations listed in this section have a policy of ecumenical hospitality to encourage all Christians to be part of the local church. This is available from the Arthur Rank Centre or the county ecumenical officer. Often there are living in rural communities men and women who commute to neighbouring towns to share in church leadership. They may feel that their leadership skills are more appropriate or more welcome in the town. They may feel more supported and better nurtured by larger congregations. But such individuals may have much to offer to the local rural church as well if their energies, skills and enthusiasm can be properly placed.

Actions

What actions would you want to recommend as a result of your audit on the ecumenical nature and potential of your church?

PART THREE

Church Life

11 Membership statistics

Take an audit

There are certain key statistics which the Church of England has considered in the past to be helpful indicators of church size and which can be used to model change, growth and decline over time. This section invites you to examine four of these statistics.

Examine the usual Sunday attendance. Select a typical month in which there are no major festivals (May is often a good choice) and calculate the average Sunday attendance over the past ten years. Are any changes noticeable?

Examine the electoral roll figures. Since 1972 electoral rolls have been revised every six years. So compare the sizes at the time of each revision in 1972, 1978, 1984, 1990, 1996 and 2002. Are any changes noticeable?

Examine the number of communicants on Easter Sunday. Go back through the service registers to look at Easter communicants at ten yearly intervals, say back at least to 1950. Are any changes noticeable?

Examine the number of communicants at Christmas midnight and on Christmas day. Go back to look at these figures at ten yearly intervals, say back at least to 1950. Are any changes noticeable?

Bench-marking

The *Rural Churches Survey* assembled statistics on usual Sunday attendance, electoral roll, Easter Day communicants and Christmas Day communicants (including midnight services). Although there may be clear limitations with all these statistics, the bench-marking exercise itself remains helpful, since at each stage we are comparing like with like. It may be helpful, for example, for one church to see how its electoral roll numbers shape up with other churches within the same size communities.

Here are the bench-marking statistics for usual Sunday attendance, electoral roll, Christmas Day communicants (including midnight), and Easter Day communicants according to community size.

Table 11: Average membership statistics by community size.

	under 200	200-399	400-899	900 plus
usual Sunday attendance	17	18	31	52
electoral roll	21	39	58	96
Christmas Day communicants	22	40	54	95
Easter Day communicants	19	34	48	79

Listening to the statistics

- The four membership statistics provide different estimates of the size of the rural church. If the figures are considered across all four community sizes a clear pattern emerges on the inter-relationship of the statistics. The most optimistic measure is provided by the electoral roll (an average of 52). The second most optimistic measure is provided by Christmas Day communicants (an average of 51). Third in line comes Easter Day (an average of 44). The least optimistic measure is provided by the usual Sunday attendance (an average of 29).
- In each community size there are fewer communicants at Easter than at Christmas. In the larger communities (900 plus) the difference is between 95 communicants at Christmas and 79 communicants at Easter.

- While all four membership statistics increase with community size, the rate of increase varies.
- Electoral roll figures may well indicate the potential for church membership. Here the figures grow in step with community size.
- In the smallest communities (under 200) usual Sunday attendance is only slightly lower than electoral rolls. Churches in larger communities show less capability of converting electoral roll members into regular churchgoers.

The new Vicar hadn't fully understood the function of the electoral roll.

Talking points

- Why do people have their names put on the electoral roll?
- Why are electoral roll members more likely to go to the services in the very small communities (under 200) than in the larger communities?

- How would you interpret electoral roll figures as an index of church membership?
- Why do you think that there are more communicants at Christmas than at Easter?
- Why should Christmas communicants relate so closely to electoral roll figures, but Easter communicants do not?
- What do you notice about the regularity with which people come to church?
- Is it true that the number of *people* who come to church is not declining, but they now come less often, so that the number of *attendances* seem to be declining?
- What happens when a rural church reduces its services from weekly to fortnightly: do the people go to services elsewhere or simply stop being weekly churchgoers?

Reflection

The relationship between Christmas and Easter communicants across the Church of England as a whole is fascinating. In recent years the number of Easter communicants has been steadily declining. The number of Christmas communicants has not declined at the same rate and sometimes even risen. There used to be more communicants at Easter than Christmas. Now there are more communicants at Christmas than at Easter. This reflects the way in which religion has a much higher profile in society as a whole at Christmas than at Easter. The churches are then able to build on the opening which is given by a secular society.

Actions

What actions would you want to recommend as a result of your audit on membership statistics?

12 Attendance at special services

Take an audit

The Church of England has rightly become discontent with publishing the usual Sunday attendance as a helpful indicator of church membership. Instead, think about those occasions when the rural church is much fuller, leaving to one side for the moment family occasions like weddings and funerals.

It is sometimes very difficult to get a true picture of attendance at special services over time. Many church registers require communicants to be counted, but are not so careful about actual attendance. Go to the registers if the information is there. If not, some good guess work will be needed.

When are the major occasions during the year that your church has especially large congregations?

- How many come to the Christmas carol services?
- How many come to the Christmas Day services (not just communicants)?
- How many come to the Christmas midnight services (not just communicants)?
- How many come to the Good Friday services?
- How many come to the Easter Sunday services (not just communicants)?
- How many come to the Mothering Sunday services?
- How many come to the Remembrance Sunday services?
- How many come to the Harvest Festival services?
- Does your church have other especially popular services?

Bench-marking

The *Rural Churches Survey* assembled statistics on attendance at services on eight special occasions which are often significant in the life and rhythm of the rural church. These occasions were:

- Christmas carol services, Christmas Day services (which often include non-eucharistic services and non-communicants attending eucharistic services),
- Christmas midnight services (which often includes people who do not receive communion),
- Good Friday services (which in some places retain significance in the rural calendar),
- Easter Sunday services (which often include non-eucharistic services and non-communicants attending eucharistic services),
- Mothering Sunday services,
- Remembrance Sunday services (which often include a significant presence from the Royal British Legion),
- Harvest Festival services (which are often the best attended of all rural services).

Here are the bench-marking statistics for attendance at this range of special services according to community size.

Table 12: Average attendance at special services by community size.

	under 200	200-399	400-899	900 plus
Christmas carol service	37	64	78	100
Christmas Day service	20	28	38	57
Christmas midnight service	9	26	44	78
Good Friday service	8	10	19	30
Easter Sunday service	28	40	60	99
Mothering Sunday service	13	33	43	75
Remembrance Sunday service	13	26	45	88
Harvest Festival service	44	59	75	96

Listening to the statistics

- The largest congregations overall are found at the Christmas carol services and the Harvest Festival services. If the figures are considered across all four community sizes, the average attendance at the Christmas carol service is 69 and the average attendance at the Harvest Festival service is 67.
- When Christmas attendance is taken into account rather than just Christmas communicants, the average across the four community sizes rises from 51 to 73.
- When Easter attendance is taken into account rather than just Easter communicants, the average across the four community sizes rises from 44 to 56.
- Harvest festivals are particularly significant in small communities (under 200) where at least a quarter of the local residents may attend.
- Remembrance Sunday services attract across all four community sizes an average congregation of 42 which puts this service in third place after the Christmas carol services and the Harvest Festival services.

GIFT AID
AND YOUR CHURCH

SPECIAL OFFER
Come at Christmas & Easter
and
then attend Harvest FREE!!!

Talking points

- How important is the Harvest Festival service in your church? What more can be done to draw more people into this service?

- How important is the Christmas carol service in your church? What can be done to draw more people into this service?
- What other opportunities are there at Christmas time (for example, family crib service) and how successful are they?
- How do you feel about those people who will come on special occasions like the Christmas carol service and the Harvest Festival, but who will not come Sunday by Sunday?
- What is the attitude to Remembrance Sunday in your church?
- Are there ways in which the Mothering Sunday service could be developed in your church? Are there links between this service and local schools?
- Overall Good Friday services do not seem well attended. Do you have ideas for changing them?

Reflection

Special services provide excellent opportunities for making links between the rural church and the local community. The use of imaginative liturgical practices can be inspirational. The aim of such services should not be primarily to recruit more people into becoming weekly churchgoers. The aim should be to keep the threshold as low as possible between the church and the community. People who come just twice a year to the Christmas carol service and to the Harvest Festival service are people who have not turned their back on the church. If the number of special services in the year could be increased, so their frequency of attendance might be increased. Moreover it is these occasional churchgoers who are most likely one day to increase their level of commitment.

Actions

What actions would you want to recommend as a result of your audit of attendance at special services?

13 Baptisms and funerals

Take an audit

Alongside special services (like the Christmas carol service and the Harvest Festival service) there are other occasions when the rural church may fill to capacity. In the smaller communities a funeral is of significance not only to the family, but to the whole village as people come to pay respects to the deceased and to offer condolences to the bereaved.

Recall how many funerals took place in your own church during the past twelve months. Estimate how many people attended these services.

The clergy from your church may also have conducted some funeral services for parishioners at the local crematorium. Find out how many services of this nature were taken for people from your community.

In the smaller communities baptism, somewhat like funerals, can take on a significance well beyond the immediate family. Friends and neighbours may want to come to support such services. Look at the baptism registers to find out how many baptisms took place in your own church during the past twelve months. How old were those being baptised?

Bench-marking

The *Rural Churches Survey* assembled statistics on the number of funerals conducted in church, and on the number of other funeral services conducted elsewhere, largely in the local crematorium. Information was also compiled on the number of infant baptisms. In the official Church of England statistics collected since1978 infants have been defined as under one year of age; and then the next category now runs up to twelve year olds. The *Rural Churches Survey* redefined infant baptism to include babies under two years of age. This definition may accord better with parents' ideas and intentions when they arrange baptism for their offspring.

Here are the bench-marking statistics for infant baptisms (under two years of age), funerals conducted in church and funerals conducted elsewhere (generally crematoria) over a twelve month period, according to community size.

Table 13: Average number of infant baptisms and funerals by community size.

	under 200	200-399	400-899	900 plus
baptisms under two years	1	3	5	9
funerals in church	1	3	4	8
funerals not in church	0	1	1	3

Listening to the statistics

- Across the four community sizes there is an average of four infant baptisms per church.
- The number of infant baptisms increase in step with the community size. While there is one baptism per year in the smallest communities (under 200), there are nine baptisms per year in the largest communities (900 plus).
- Across the four community sizes there are four funerals conducted in church for every one conducted elsewhere. The ratio seems to decrease in the larger communities. In the smaller communities the natural option seems to be to go for a church funeral.

- While the number of funerals in each community per year seems quite low, for the priest with six or seven parishes, the numbers soon build up.

Talking points

- Do you think infant baptism should be available for all parents who ask for it?
- Should your church offer a 'naming ceremony' as an option which some parents may prefer?

- Should we expect parents who want their infants baptised to become regular churchgoers?
- How do you feel about your church baptising the grandchildren of local residents although the baby's parents live elsewhere?
- What kind of follow-up care does your church provide for the infants who have been baptised and for their parents?
- How important is a funeral service in church for the bereaved?
- How can funeral services be made most helpful for the bereaved?
- What pastoral care can your church offer to the bereaved and how are lay people involved in this ministry?

Reflection

Many parents still come seeking baptism for their babies, although they themselves do not play an active part in church life. Currently there are two approaches to such requests offered by different Church of England parishes. Some offer a more 'closed' baptism policy, emphasise the seriousness of the promises which the parents make, and expect evidence of Christian commitment, learning and church attendance. Others offer a more 'open' baptism policy, emphasise the unrestricted bounty of God's grace, and seek baptism as an opportunity to affirm the parents' interest in a Christian sacrament. Many rural churches recognise the pastoral benefits of a more open baptism policy. How are the bereaved supported? Who in your parish is trained in bereavement care?

Actions

What actions would you want to recommend as a result of your audit on baptisms and funerals?

14 Church activities

Take an audit

There are a number of ways in which rural churches are able to nurture the commitment of their regular members and also to extend their outreach into the wider local community. This section examines three different forms of activity.

First, examine what your local church does by way of study groups.

- Do you have a regular pattern of study, bible, prayer or discussion groups? If so, how often do they meet?
- Do you have a special pattern of study groups during Lent?
- What pattern of study groups have taken place in the past?

Second, give attention to church groups like the choir and the bellringers.

- Do you have a church choir?
- What has been the history of church choirs in your church?
- Does your church have bells? If so, do you have a band of ringers?
- What has been the history of bellringing in your church?

Third, give attention to the parish magazine or newsletter.

- Does your church have a magazine or newsletter?
- Who is responsible for producing the magazine or newsletter?
- Who receives the magazine or newsletter?
- What has been the history of the parish magazine or newsletter in your church?

Bench-marking

The *Rural Churches Survey* assembled statistics on church choirs, bellringers, church magazines, and study, bible, prayer or discussion groups. The key information concerns whether or not the church has a choir, whether or not the church has a band of ringers, and whether or not the church produces a magazine or newsletter. The definitions and distinctions between study groups, discussion groups, bible groups and prayer groups are quite problematic. The key information concerns whether or not the church has a group of some sort and, if so, how often the group meets.

Here are the bench-marking statistics for church activities, identified by the four headings of choir, ringers, magazine and groups according to community size.

Table 14: Proportions of churches supporting specified activities by community size.

	under 200 %	200-399 %	400-899 %	900 plus %
choir	11	26	43	62
ringers	18	29	42	44
magazine or newsletter	86	88	91	88
study, bible, prayer, discussion groups				
weekly	5	10	17	25
monthly	7	14	17	19
sometimes	33	37	56	48

Listening to the statistics

- Across all four community sizes, one in three (34%) rural churches have a church choir.
- Likelihood of a church choir is closely related to community size, ranging from 11% of churches in small communities (under 200) to 62% of churches in larger communities (900 plus).

- Across all four community sizes, one in three (32%) of rural churches have a band of ringers.
- Likelihood of a band of ringers is clearly related to community size (but less so than in the case of choirs), ranging from 18% of churches in small communities (under 200) to 44% of churches in larger communities (900 plus).
- Across all four community sizes almost nine out of every ten churches (87%) have a magazine or newsletter, and there is little variation between the smaller and the larger communities.
- The provision of a study, bible, prayer, or discussion group is clearly related to community size. Half (51%) of the churches in communities under 200 never have such a group. The proportions which never have a group fall to 30% of the churches in communities between 200 and 399, 10% of the churches in communities between 400 and 899 and 8% of the churches in communities with 900 or more inhabitants.

Miss Freeman has started a young choir. They sing very well, and it is hoped that when they get a little older the congregation will be able to see them.

Talking points

- What advantages does a church choir bring to church life?

- What are the possibilities of starting or strengthening the choir in your church?
- What advantages does a band of ringers bring to church life?
- If you have a band of ringers can this be strengthened?
- If you have a ring of bells, but no local ringers, would it be possible to start such a band?
- How easy does your church find it to support a study, bible, prayer or discussion group?
- Can more be done to involve churchgoers and the wider local community in discussion groups?
- What is the purpose of a church magazine?
- Does the magazine go to every household?
- How attractive and successful do you regard your church magazine? Can things be done to make it even better?

Reflection

You do not need professional musicians to make a church choir, but you do need people who can sing in tune and who are willing to make a fairly regular commitment, particularly a leader. There are two great benefits to church life brought by a church choir. First, the choir is there to help the singing. Singing still plays a central part in Anglican worship and with small congregations can become very difficult and at times embarrassing. The role of leading the singing can be an important ministry. Second, belonging to the choir can help to foster commitment to the church and can sometimes attract others into membership. For example, young people can be encouraged to serve the church in that way and those who live alone or who attend church alone can be helped to feel part of a group.

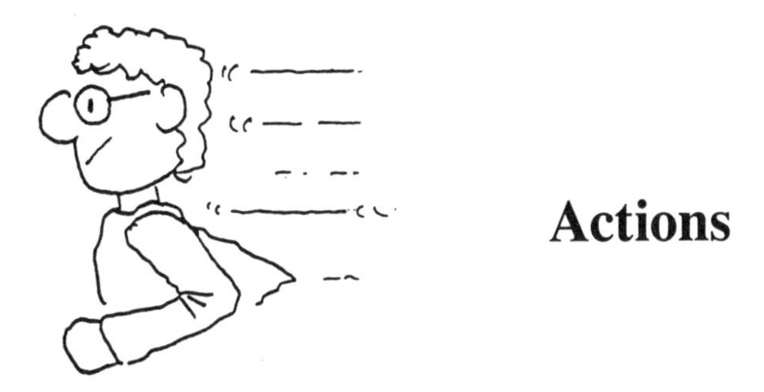

Actions

What actions would you want to recommend as a result of your audit on church activities?

15 Away days

Take an audit

A congregation may meet every Sunday for a service, but there is so little time then for people to meet together, to share ideas, and to discuss their vision for the church's future. A PCC may meet at least four times a year and discuss the essential business which underpins the life of the church, but there is so little time to really scratch the surface of what matters, and it can be difficult to engage the rest of the local church. There may be a regular discussion group, but it is likely that this group will touch only a small proportion of the regular congregation.

For all of these reasons some churches find it very beneficial to go away for a day or for a weekend, say to the Cathedral to the diocesan conference or retreat centre. Examine what your church does in this way.

- Has your church had a day away for study, prayer, or planning in the past three years?
- Has your church had a weekend away for study, prayer, or planning in the past three years?

Bench-marking

The *Rural Churches Survey* assembled statistics on the numbers of churches which had taken a day away for study within the past three years and the number of churches which had taken a weekend away for study in the past three years.

Here are the bench-marking statistics for the proportions of churches which had taken a day away for study or a weekend away for study in the past three years according to community size.

Table 15: Proportions of churches taking a day or a weekend away for study in the past three years by community size.

	under 200 %	200-399 %	400-899 %	900 plus %
day away	8	13	12	17
weekend away	2	5	5	10

Listening to the statistics

- Across all four community sizes, one in seven (13%) rural churches had taken a day away for study, prayer, or discussion over the past three years.
- Likelihood of churches taking a day away for study is related to community size, ranging from 8% of churches in small communities (under 200) to 17% of churches in larger communities (900 plus).
- Across all four community sizes, one in seventeen (6%) rural churches had taken a weekend away for study, prayer, or discussion over the past three years.
- Likelihood of churches taking a weekend away for study is related to community size, ranging from 2% of churches in small communities (under 200) to 10% of churches in larger communities (900 plus).

St Cyril's Little Doze 1999 Weekend Everest Expedition

Talking points

- What are the advantages of the local church going away for a day or for weekend together?
- How willing would your own church be to go away for a day or a weekend together?

- What setting could be the most helpful to go for a day or for a weekend?
- How best could the agenda be set for a day or for a weekend away?
- What would encourage or discourage people joining in with such a day or weekend?
- Are there advantages in your church going away with other churches in the benefice?
- Are there disadvantages in your church going away with other churches in the benefice?

Reflection

Great benefits can come from members of the local church going away together, perhaps with other churches in the benefice, (for a day or for a weekend) to study, to pray, to discuss, and plan and to seek God's will together. There can also be risks in bringing together a group of people who are not used to working together in this way and who may have very different backgrounds, aptitudes and agendas. Remember that not everyone is at ease in groups. Parishes new to such methods should slowly introduce the length and depth of such days and get professional help in organising them. The local church could engage an outside facilitator who is skilled in group processes.

Actions

What actions would you want to recommend as a result of your audit on away days?

PART FOUR

The Church Building

16 Accessibility and security

Take an audit

The accessibility and security of the church building is a matter of central importance to every rural congregation.

Undertake an audit on how accessible your church is to residents and to visitors.

- Is the church kept locked at night?
- Is the church kept locked during the day?
- If the church is locked, is it easy to discover how to find the key?
- Are other churches in the area kept open or kept locked?
- When was the current policy determined for your church, and by whom?
- What do your church insurers require in respect of locks?

Undertake an audit on the damage which your church has suffered.

- What vandalism has your church suffered in the last ten years?
- What theft has your church suffered in the last ten years?
- How have theft and vandalism related to your church being kept locked or open?
- What level of theft and vandalism have neighbouring churches suffered in the last ten years?

Bench-marking

The *Rural Churches Survey* assembled information on whether rural churches were kept locked or kept open. This issue was explored with five main categories of response: never locked, locked only at night, open at specified times most days, locked with a key holder named and locked without a key holder named. The *Rural Churches Survey* also assembled information on whether rural churches had suffered theft or vandalism within the last ten years.

Here are the bench-marking statistics for the accessibility and security of rural churches according to community size. Security is assessed in terms of whether the church has suffered theft or vandalism at least once within the past ten years.

Table 16: Proportions of churches kept locked, and which have suffered theft and vandalism by community size.

	under 200 %	200-399 %	400-899 %	900 plus %
never locked	34	21	16	7
locked only at night	22	23	41	35
open at specified times most days	1	3	3	5
locked with named key holder	26	35	27	35
locked without named key holder	17	18	13	19
suffered theft in last ten years	30	34	44	47
suffered vandalism in last ten years	15	27	33	46

Listening to the statistics

- Across all four community sizes, one in five (20%) of rural churches are never locked and a further 30% are locked only at night. A handful (3%) are unlocked at specified times each day.
- Across all four community sizes, nearly half (48%) of rural churches are kept locked.
- Across all four community sizes, a third (35%) of the churches which are kept locked have no key holder named.
- The smaller the community, the greater is the likelihood of the church being kept unlocked day and night. In small communities (under 200) 34% of churches are kept unlocked day and night, while the proportion falls to 7% in larger communities (900 plus).
- Across all four community sizes, nearly two-fifths (40%) of rural churches have suffered theft in the past ten years.
- Across all four community sizes, nearly one-third (30%) of rural churches have suffered vandalism in the past ten years.
- Churches in larger communities (900 plus) are fifty percent more likely than churches in small communities (under 200) to have suffered theft in the past ten

years (47% compared with 30%).

- Churches in larger communities (900 plus) are three times more likely than churches in small communities (under 200) to have suffered vandalism in the past ten years (46% compared with 15%).

'No, it's not to keep the vandals out, it's to keep his small congregation in!'

Talking points

- Does keeping the church locked reduce incidents of theft?
- Does keeping the church locked reduce incidents of vandalism?

- What message does a locked church send out to the local community?
- What message does a locked church send out to visitors?
- How willing are people to steward your church when it is kept open?
- How willing are members of the congregation to call into the church whenever they are passing to keep an eye on things?
- How viable would it be to install security cameras?
- Can the church's valuable possessions be kept secure even when the church is unlocked?
- Why do people vandalise churches, and who are these people?
- What can be done to help protect churches from vandalism?

Reflection

The debate between accessibility and security is a complex one. Some would take the view that a church is like a private house and that the people who regularly worship in the church have a responsibility to take all reasonable precautions to safeguard the building and its contents. Others would take the view that the church building is there to offer to everyone a holy space in which to pray and a window into the love of God for all people. According to this view, a locked church is a defeated church. Evidence suggests that locking the church may actually increase criminal damage. *Rural Visitors* (published by ACORA in 2001) is based on a survey of visitors to 161 churches and has detailed sections on security and the ministry of welcome.

Actions

What actions would you want to recommend as a result of your audit on the accessibility and security of your church?

17 Facilities

Take an audit

Take a close look at your church building and undertake an audit of the current facilities. Consider three specific issues.

First, examine the basic facilities which contribute to the level of comfort associated with regular use of the church for worship.

- Is the general level of lighting adequate?
- Is the general level of heating sufficient?

Second, examine the extent to which the church meets current standards and expectations for public buildings.

- Is there access for the disabled?
- Are toilets easily accessible, either in the church or in a nearby building?

Third, examine how useful the church is for wider church purposes.

- Is there a separate room for meetings?
- Is there an identified area for social gatherings?
- Are there facilities for making hot drinks?

Then consider how your church compares in these three ways with other churches in the area.

Bench-marking

The *Rural Churches Survey* provided a checklist in respect of seven facilities: adequate lighting, sufficient heating, access for the disabled, accessible toilets, a small room for meetings, an area for social gatherings and facilities for making hot drinks.

Here are the bench-marking statistics for the facilities provided by rural churches according to community size.

Table 17: Proportions of churches providing specified facilities by community size.

	under 200 %	200-399 %	400-899 %	900 plus %
adequate lighting	68	76	85	89
sufficient heating	48	62	71	72
access for the disabled	21	30	35	45
accessible toilet	9	13	23	46
small room for meetings	2	6	12	19
area for social gatherings	5	14	22	34
facilities for hot drinks	19	32	48	67

Listening to the statistics

- Across all four community sizes, four out of five (79%) churches assess their lighting as adequate. The proportion rises from 68% in small communities (under 200) to 89% in larger communities (900 plus).
- Across all four community sizes, two-thirds (63%) of churches assess their heating as sufficient. The proportion rises from 48% in small communities (under 200) to 72% in larger communities (900 plus).
- Across all four community sizes, one-third (33%) of churches have access for the disabled. The proportion rises from 21% in small communities (under 200) to 45% in larger communities (900 plus).
- Across all four community sizes, between one-fifth and one-quarter (22%) of

churches have accessible toilets. While toilets are accessible in 46% of churches in larger communities (900 plus), the proportion falls to 9% in small communities (under 200).

- The extent to which churches have facilities for social activities is clearly related to size. In communities of under 200 inhabitants, 2% of churches have a small room for meetings, 5% have an area for social gatherings and 19% have facilities for making hot drinks. In communities with 900 or more inhabitants, 19% of churches have a small room for meetings, 34% have an area for social gatherings and 67% have facilities for making hot drinks.

Talking points

- How important do you feel adequate lighting is in churches?
- What can be done to enhance the lighting in your church?
- How important do you feel sufficient heating is in churches?
- What can be done to enhance the heating in your church?
- How well prepared is your church for giving access to the disabled?
- How could toilet facilities be improved in your church?
- How well equipped is your church for holding social events and public meetings?
- How easy would it be to improve the kitchen facilities in your church?
- Could part of your church be re-modelled into a convenient, comfortable and warm room for meetings?

Reflection

Many of our precious rural churches were built in an age which had very different ideas of human comfort from our own generation. Expectations about public buildings have changed radically in the past fifty years. These changed expectations present the rural church with a considerable quandary. The problem is to find ways of making these buildings really useful for the twenty-first century, while at the same time preserving the integrity of their historic and irreplaceable past.

Actions

What actions would you want to recommend as a result of your audit on the facilities of your church?

18 Recent changes

Take an audit

When we are accustomed to worshipping in a church week by week, our concept of change may become distorted. On the one hand, for some people it is all too easy to forget how much is changing and to imagine that things are making less progress than they really are. On the other hand, for other people, it is all too easy to forget for how long some things have just stood still. Such people will talk about a specific change that took place a few years ago, and then be very surprised to find that the change had really been implemented in the late 1970s.

Make a list of all the changes that have taken place in your church in the past *five* years.

- Has a new heating system been installed?
- Has a new lighting system been installed?
- Has the organ been repaired or replaced?
- Have any pews been removed?
- Has the altar been repositioned?
- Has a social space been created inside the church?
- Have new toilets been provided?
- Has a new kitchen been provided?
- Have changes been made to help access for the disabled?

Bench-marking

The *Rural Churches Survey* provided a checklist in respect of nine possible changes which might have occurred during the past five years: new heating system, new lighting system, new organ, removal of pews, repositioning of altar, creation of social space within the church, provision of toilets, provision of a kitchen and improving access for the disabled.

Here are the bench-marking statistics for the changes that have taken place in rural churches over the past five years, according to community size.

Table 18: Proportions of churches initiating specified changes within the past five years by community size.

	under 200 %	200-399 %	400-899 %	900 plus %
new heating system	10	15	18	19
new lighting system	9	11	17	11
new organ	10	10	6	7
removal of pews	1	4	9	10
repositioning of altar	2	6	6	9
social space inside church	2	4	8	7
provision of toilet	0	2	2	7
provision of kitchen	0	1	2	7
access for disabled	1	1	1	6

Listening to the statistics

- The biggest push for change in rural churches over the past five years has concerned the installation of new heating systems. Across all four community sizes, 15% of rural churches had new heating systems during this period. This was the case for 10% of churches in small communities (under 200), and for 19% of churches in larger communities (900 plus).
- The second biggest push for change in rural churches over the past five years has

concerned the installation of new lighting systems. Across all four community sizes, 12% of rural churches had new lighting systems during this period. This was the case for 9% of churches in small communities (under 200), for 11% of churches in communities between 200 and 399 inhabitants, for 17% of churches in communities between 400 and 899 inhabitants, and 11% of churches in communities of 900 plus inhabitants.

- The third biggest push for change in rural churches over the past five years has concerned the acquisition of a new organ. Across all four community sizes 9% of rural churches had new organs during this period. In this case, the smaller communities were more likely to have acquired a new organ than the larger communities. This may reflect small churches replacing costly pipe organs with much cheaper electric organs.
- Apart from these three priority areas over the past five years, comparatively little change has been initiated in rural churches. Across all four community sizes 6% had removed pews, 6% had repositioned the altar, 5% had created social space within the building, 3% had made new provisions for a kitchen, 3% had made new provision for a toilet, and 2% had improved access for the disabled.

'Oh yes, they still talk about the installation of the first toilet. It all coincided with the news of Wellington's victory at Waterloo!'

Talking points

- Have rural churches got their priorities right in putting heating, lighting and the organ at the top of their list for improvements?
- How adequate is the organ in your church? Do you feel that any improvement is necessary?
- Could your church be improved by redesigning the security, and how would people feel about this?
- Could the liturgy in your church be improved by repositioning the altar, and what effect would this have on the worship?
- What would need to be done to make your church more accessible for the disabled?
- What changes would you most like to see made to your church building?

Reflection

Changes made to rural churches face three huge obstacles. First, there is an obstacle of local opinion. In particular it is those people who may not attend services all that often who are likely to resent changes being made to 'their' church. Second, there is the obstacle of the necessary facilities. The procedure may take time and trouble, but is there as an important safeguard for the church's heritage. Third, there is an obstacle of cost. People have to be really convinced by a project before they will dig into their pockets to pay for it.

Actions

What actions would you want to recommend as a result of your audit on the changes made to your church over the past five years?

19 Church-related activities

Take an audit

The church building is a costly but very important asset for the church in rural communities. It is the place where the congregation meets to worship Sunday by Sunday. It is a sacred site which witnesses to the Christian faith, to the local residents and to the visitors. More than this, the church building can be used as a resource for the local church's whole programme of ministry and mission. This is especially important in communities which have no church hall, no church school and no parsonage.

Undertake an audit of the ways in which your church building is used for church-related activities. The next section will turn attention to community-related activities.

- Is your church used for coffee after the service?
- Is your church used for church meetings?
- Is your church used for choir practice?
- Is your church used for selling Christian literature?
- Is your church used for an annual harvest lunch or supper?
- Is your church used for children's activities?
- Is your church used for youth activities?
- Is your church used for a play group?
- Is your church used as a parish office?
- Is your church used for other church-related activities?

Bench-marking

The *Rural Churches Survey* assembled information on a range of ways in which rural church buildings were being used to support the ministry and mission of the local church. The following issues emerged as particularly interesting:

- serving coffee after services,
- holding church meetings (sometimes after the service and sometimes on other occasions),
- conducting choir practice,
- selling Christian literature (both to the regular congregation and to visitors),
- providing an environment for the annual harvest lunch or supper,
- being used for children's activities,
- being used for youth activities,
- being used for a play group,
- making space for the parish office.

Here are the bench-marking statistics for the ways in which rural churches are used for church-related activities, according to community size.

Table 19: Proportions of churches used for specific church-related activities by community size.

	under 200 %	200-399 %	400-899 %	900 plus %
coffee after services	47	58	74	78
church meetings	29	41	49	57
choir practice	7	21	38	54
selling Christian literature	5	14	21	28
annual harvest lunch/supper	8	11	9	16
children's activities	3	15	21	29
youth activities	1	4	6	11
play group	1	2	1	6
parish office	0	0	3	6

Listening to the statistics

- Overall the churches in larger communities are more likely to be used for a range of church-related activities than the churches in smaller communities.
- Overall two-thirds (64%) of rural churches are used for coffee after services, ranging from 47% in smaller communities (under 200) to 78% in larger communities (900 plus).
- Overall one in ten (11%) of rural churches are used for an annual harvest lunch or supper, ranging from 8% in small communities (under 200) to 16% in larger communities (900 plus).
- Overall two-fifths (43%) of rural churches are used for church meetings, ranging from 29% in small communities (under 200) to 57% in larger communities (900 plus).
- Overall between a quarter and a third (29%) of rural churches are used for choir practices, ranging from 7% in small communities (under 200) to 54% in larger communities (900 plus).
- Overall rural churches are not used a great deal for work among children and young people. Across all four community sizes, 16% are used for children's activities and 5% for youth activities.

'You must come to our new Bistro in the church Nave. We've called it 'Pew-Fodder'

Talking points

- Does your church make enough use of the opportunity for refreshments and social interaction after services?
- How suitable is your church for holding church meetings?
- What would be the easiest way to make your church more useful for meetings?
- Is your church making the best use of opportunities to sell Christian literature?
- Have you tried using your church for occasions like a harvest lunch? How suitable is the building and what would people think about this?
- Are there ways in which your church could be better used for activities among children and young people?
- Would it be helpful to create a parish office in your church?

Reflection

The church building is very expensive to maintain for use for one hour only on a Sunday. There are many ways in which the ministry and mission of the church needs a suitable building in which to meet, especially after so many rural parsonages have been sold and so many rural church schools closed. Adapting the church to serve the needs of the Christian community more effectively may be an important priority in the next decade.

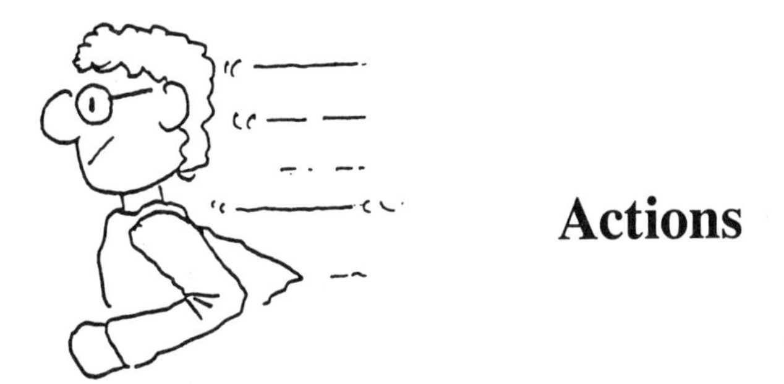

Actions

What actions would you want to recommend as a result of your audit on the church-related activities for which your church is used?

20 Community-related activities

Take an audit

The church building is not simply, or even primarily, the property of the local congregation. In a real sense that building properly belongs to the whole local community. It is part of the village's rightful heritage. Tradition has it that at various times in history the church building served secular as well as religious functions. In the twenty-first century this secret is being rediscovered.

Undertake an audit of the ways in which your church building is used for community-related activities.

- Is your church used for musical entertainment?
- Is your church used for art exhibitions?
- Is your church used for dramatic performances?
- Is your church used for evening social activities?
- Is your church used for coffee mornings?
- Is your church used for lunch meetings for the elderly?
- Is your church used for tourist information?
- Is your church used for displaying public information?
- Is your church used for any other community-related activities?

Bench-marking

The *Rural Churches Survey* assembled information on a range of ways in which rural church buildings were being used to support community-related activities. The following issues emerged as particularly interesting: the use of churches like a concert hall for musical entertainment, the use of churches like an art gallery for art exhibitions, the use of churches like a theatre for dramatic performances, the use of churches for coffee mornings and for social evenings, and the use of churches like a community hall to have lunch meetings for the elderly. Churches are also used to display public information and to provide information for tourists.

Here are the bench-marking statistics for the ways in which rural churches are used for community-related activities, according to community size.

Table 20: Proportions of churches used for specific community-related activities by community size.

	under 200 %	200-399 %	400-899 %	900 plus %
musical entertainment	26	47	54	62
displaying public information	20	24	35	43
art exhibition	6	14	15	10
dramatic performances	3	9	15	19
evening social activities	4	4	6	13
coffee mornings	2	2	8	16
tourist information	4	5	5	8
lunch meetings for the elderly	0	0	1	1

Listening to the statistics

- Overall the churches in larger communities are more likely to be used for a range of community-related activities than the churches in smaller communities.
- Overall nearly half (47%) of rural churches are used for musical entertainment, ranging from 26% in small communities (under 200) to 62% in larger communities (900 plus).
- Second in line after their use as a concert hall, rural churches are used as art galleries and as theatres. Across all four community sizes 11% of rural churches are used as art galleries and 11% of rural churches are used as theatres.
- While just 6% of churches in communities under 200 have hosted art exhibitions, the proportions rise to 15% in communities between 400 and 899 and fall again to 10% in communities over 900 inhabitants.
- While just 3% of churches in communities under 200 have hosted dramatic performances, the proportions rise to 15% in communities between 400 and 899 and to 19% in communities over 900 inhabitants.
- Across all four community sizes 7% of rural churches host coffee mornings or evening social activities.

Talking points

- Apart from the church, what other public buildings are available in your community?
- Could more use be made of the church building in serving the needs of the community?

- How would people feel about the church being used for concerts?
- How would people feel about the church being used for art exhibitions?
- How would people feel about the church being used for dramatic presentations?
- How would people feel about the church being used for a lunch club for the elderly?
- Would the local community value the church being made available for community-related activities?
- Would the use of the church for community-related activities release new sources of funding for its upkeep?

Reflection

Often rural churches are of considerable historic interest and play a key part in the life of the village as well as in the life of the congregation. There are good reasons for sharing these churches more with the local community. On the one hand, many rural communities lack other forms of public space in which to meet. The community needs the church building. On the other hand, many congregations are very hard pressed to maintain the historic church as well as to provide an increasing share of the costs for the ministry of the vicar and diocese. The congregation needs support from the community. Moreover, the use of the church for community-related activities will help to keep the church at the centre of local attention.

Actions

What actions would you want to recommend as a result of your audit on the community-related activities for which your church is used?

PART FIVE

Every Member Ministry

21 Ministries of administration

Take an audit

For a long time the word 'ministry' seems to have been captured by the clerical profession. What the vicar did was called 'ministry', what other people undertook toward the life and ministry of the local church was something different from ministry. Those days are now behind us.

Today we are becoming accustomed to value all the functions needed to sustain and to develop the life of the local church as ministry. Clergy and lay people work together and collaborate in shared ministry. For simple analytical purposes this workbook distinguishes between four aspects of every member ministry, characterised here as administration, education, pastoral care and liturgy. All these ministries are of high importance in the local church and require specific gifts, aptitudes, skills and training. Some people may combine ministries across these areas, while other people may prefer to concentrate their energy primarily in one area.

Take an audit of the extent to which lay people are involved in your church in the ministry of administration.

- Are lay people involved in office administration?
- Are lay people involved in producing the church magazine?
- Are lay people involved in routine maintenance?
- Are lay people involved in churchyard care?
- Are lay people involved in organising fundraising?
- Are lay people involved in organising social events?
- Are lay people involved in other ministries of administration?

Bench-marking

The *Rural Churches Survey* assembled information on the extent to which rural churches were supported by lay people being involved in the ministries of administration. This aspect of every member ministry was explored through giving particular attention to the following ministries: office administration, producing the church magazine, routine building maintenance, churchyard care, cleaning the church, organising fundraising and organising social events.

Here are the bench-marking statistics for lay participation in the every member ministries of administration according to community size.

Table 21: Proportions of churches in which lay people engage in specified ministries of administration by community size.

	under 200 %	200-399 %	400-899 %	900 plus %
office administration	18	26	30	41
producing church magazine	37	48	66	74
routine maintenance	77	84	87	85
churchyard care	84	85	83	82
cleaning the church	92	94	95	97
organising fund raising	79	89	90	91
organising social events	63	79	84	84

Listening to the statistics

- There are hardly any rural churches where lay people are not crucially involved in the ministry of administration.
- Across all four community sizes, lay people share the ministry of cleaning in 94% of the churches. There is very little variation according to community size.
- Across all four community sizes, lay people share the ministry of churchyard care in 84% of the churches. There is very little variation according to community size.

- In very small communities (under 200) there is less lay involvement in the ministry of organising fundraising (79%), compared with about 90% in larger communities.
- In very small communities (under 200) there is less lay involvement in the ministry of organising social events (63%), compared with between 79% and 84% in communities of 200 plus inhabitants.
- In very small communities (under 200) there is less lay involvement in the ministry of routine maintenance (77%), compared with between 84% and 87% in communities of 200 plus inhabitants.
- In very small communities (under 200) there is less lay involvement in the ministry of office administration (18%), compared with a steady increase to 26% in communities between 200 and 399, to 30% in communities between 400 and 899, and to 41% in communities of 900 plus inhabitants.
- Lay participation in producing the parish magazine rises from 37% in communities under 200, to 48% in communities between 200 and 399, to 66% in communities between 400 and 899, and to 74% in communities of 900 plus inhabitants.

Talking points

- How is the life and witness of your church affected by the cleanliness of the building?
- Does the state of your churchyard communicate an awareness that someone cares?
- How important to the church council is a programme of routine maintenance?
- Is the life and witness of your church affected by its approach to fundraising?
- Is the organising of social events an effective witness to the life of your church?
- Is your church magazine a witness to the church in your community?
- Is the life and witness of your church made more effective by the administration in the parish office?
- How are all the ministries above carried out?
- Are all the ministries properly valued in your church?
- How can others be drawn into the ministries above?

Reflection

The ministries of administration are crucial to the maintenance and growth of the rural church. Churches which are untidy and dirty detract from the services held in them. Churches, which are in need of routine maintenance and set in un-cared for churchyards, proclaim the message of neglect and irrelevance to the community and lack of love for individuals. Churches where there is inadequate administration and low levels of fundraising cease to be able to fulfil other areas of ministry and mission.

Actions

What actions would you want to recommend as a result of your audit on the every member ministries of administration?

22 Ministries of education

Take an audit

There is a range of different ministries which are crucial to the life of the local church. The proper rediscovery of 'every member ministry' exercised by the whole People of God as the Body of Christ is transforming the rural church. For simple analytic purposes this workbook distinguishes between four aspects of every member ministry; characterised here as administration, education, pastoral care and liturgy. All these ministries are of high importance in the local church and require specific gifts, aptitudes, skills and training. Some people may combine ministries across these areas, while other people may prefer to concentrate their energy on one area.

Take an audit of the extent to which lay people are involved in your church in the ministry of education. In this connection distinguish between two spheres of educational ministry. Begin with educational ministries among children and young people.

- Are lay people involved in a Sunday school?
- Are lay people involved in a church youth club?
- Are lay people involved in a church sponsored uniformed group?
- Are lay people involved in a church sponsored play group?
- Are lay people involved in other ministries of education among children and young people?

Now turn your attention to educational ministries among adults.

- Are lay people involved in leading a discussion group?
- Are lay people involved in leading a prayer group?
- Are lay people involved in other ministries of education among adults?

Bench-marking

The *Rural Churches Survey* assembled information on the extent to which rural churches were supported by lay people being involved in the ministries of education. This aspect of every member ministry was explored through giving particular attention to the following ministries among children and young people: Sunday school including after school clubs and Saturday workshops, church youth club, and church sponsored uniformed groups (including Cubs, Brownies, Scouts, Guides, Boys Brigade, Girls Brigade, Church Lads' and Church Girls' Brigade). Attention was also given to the following ministries among adults: leading discussion groups (which can be based on the bible or on other materials) and leading prayer groups.

Here are the bench-marking statistics for lay participation in the every member ministries of education according to community size.

Table 22: Proportions of churches in which lay people engage in specified ministries of education by community size.

	under 200 %	200-399 %	400-899 %	900 plus %
Sunday school	18	31	51	68
church youth club	3	9	17	23
church sponsored uniformed group	1	3	6	13
church sponsored play group	2	0	6	6
leading discussion group	12	28	39	57
leading prayer group	9	16	25	38

Listening to the statistics

- Across all four community sizes, lay people share an educational ministry through Sunday school type activities in two out of every five (41%) rural churches.
- Lay people are almost four times as likely to be involved in Sunday school type educational ministries in communities of 900 plus (68%) than in communities of under 200 (18%).

- Across all four community sizes, three times as many churches benefit from lay people offering educational ministries in Sunday school type activities (41%) as in youth type activities (13%).
- Lay involvement in church youth clubs is present in 3% of churches in communities under 200 inhabitants, and rises to 9% in communities between 200 and 399, to 17% in communities between 400 and 899, and to 23% in communities of 900 plus inhabitants.
- Across all four community sizes there is lay involvement in church sponsored uniformed groups in 6% of rural churches.
- Across all four community sizes there is lay involvement in church sponsored play groups in 3% of rural churches.
- Across all four community sizes a third (33%) of rural churches benefit from lay leadership of discussion groups, ranging from 12% of churches in small communities (under 200) to 57% of churches in larger communities (900 plus).
- Across all four community sizes two-fifths (22%) of rural churches benefit from lay leadership of prayer groups, ranging from 9% of churches in small communities (under 200) to 38% of churches in larger communities (900 plus).

Mr Simpkins, the Study Group leader takes the Old Testament sessions very seriously.

Talking points

- What opportunities has your church for developing new ministries among children of Sunday school age, and who might be involved as leaders?

- What opportunities has your church for developing new ministries among pre-schoolers, and who might be involved?
- What opportunities has your church for developing new ministries among young people who are outgrowing the Sunday school age range, and who might be involved?
- What benefits could your church derive from more discussion groups or more house groups, and who could lead such groups?
- What links exist between church and school? How could they be developed?
- At the school are there Christian governors, cleaners, cooks, helpers, teachers? How is their ministry supported by the church?

Reflection

Ministry among children and young people is being taken more seriously across the denominations. It is increasingly recognised that Christian parents and churches have responsibility and an obligation to take the Christian nurture of young people seriously. Life experiences give many adults something they can properly share with young people. This personal relationship, which can benefit both sides, should be encouraged. Congregations include some people who are professionally qualified as teachers who may well be willing to help other church members acquire professional skills in ministries among children and young people. It is always required to follow diocesan guidelines and policies on child protection and to have all volunteers and paid staff involved in ministry among young people properly registered and formally checked.

Actions

What actions would you want to recommend as a result of your audit on the every member ministries of education?

23 Ministries of pastoral care

Take an audit

There is a range of different ministries which are crucial to the life of the local church. The proper rediscovery of 'every member ministry' exercised by the whole People of God as the Body of Christ is transforming the rural church. For simple analytic purposes this workbook distinguishes between four aspects of every member ministry; characterised here as administration, education, pastoral care and liturgy. All these ministries are of high importance in the local church and require specific gifts, aptitudes, skills and training. Some people may combine ministries across these areas, while other people may prefer to concentrate their energy on one area.

Take an audit of the extent to which lay people are involved in your church in the ministries of pastoral care. In this connection consider three specific areas of pastoral care. Begin with the pastoral care ministries of meeting with people in their homes.

- Are lay people involved in visiting the sick?
- Are lay people involved in visiting the bereaved?
- Are lay people involved in taking communion to the housebound?
- Are lay people involved in other similar ministries of pastoral care?

Second, turn your attention to pastoral care ministries which prepare people for significant rites of passage. These ministries may also be educational in nature, but often have a primary focus on pastoral care.

- Are lay people involved in confirmation preparation?
- Are lay people involved in baptism preparation?
- Are lay people involved in marriage preparation?
- Are lay people involved in other similar ministries of pastoral care?

Third, turn your attention to pastoral care ministries which are concerned with welcome and with community life.

- Are lay people involved in serving refreshments after the service?
- Are lay people involved in other similar ministries of pastoral care?

Bench-marking

The *Rural Churches Survey* assembled information on the extent to which rural churches were supported by lay people being involved in the ministries of pastoral care. This aspect of every member ministry gives particular attention to three components of pastoral care. Pastoral care exercised by visiting people in their homes was explored through visiting the sick, visiting the bereaved and taking communion to the housebound. Pastoral care exercised by preparation for major rites of passage was explored through baptism preparation, confirmation preparation and marriage preparation. Pastoral care exercised by concern for welcome and community life was explored through serving refreshments after the service.

Here are the bench-marking statistics for lay participation in the every member ministries of pastoral care according to community size.

Table 23: Proportions of churches in which lay people engage in specified ministries of pastoral care by community size.

	under 200 %	200-399 %	400-899 %	900 plus %
visiting the sick	42	51	56	67
visiting the bereaved	26	36	45	42
taking communion to the housebound	4	7	6	17
confirmation preparation	4	7	11	16
baptism preparation	3	5	8	12
marriage preparation	3	3	5	6
serving refreshments after service	42	56	67	82

Listening to the statistics

- The ministry of meeting with people in their homes clearly distinguishes between different reasons for visiting. Across all four community sizes, lay people share in the ministry of visiting the sick in one out of every two churches (53%). The proportion of churches in which lay people share in the ministry of visiting the bereaved drops to one in every three (36%). The proportion of churches in which lay people share in the ministry of taking communion to the housebound drops to one in every twelve (8%).

- Comparatively few churches have involved lay people in pastoral care ministries concerned with preparing people for major rites of passage. Across all four community sizes, lay people share in confirmation preparation in 9% of churches, in baptism preparation in 7% of churches, and in marriage preparation in 4% of churches.
- Three out of every five (61%) of rural churches across the four community sizes benefit from lay people being involved in serving refreshments after services.
- Lay involvement in ministries of pastoral care are clearly correlated with community size. For example, lay participation in the ministry of visiting the sick varies from 42% of churches in small communities (under 200) to 67% of churches in larger communities (900 plus). Similarly lay participation in the ministry of serving refreshments after services varies from 42% of churches in small communities (under 200) to 82% of churches in larger communities (900 plus).

'After the service please stay for our 'Happy Hour'. This week there is a special offer on Malt Whiskey and beer is still only £1 a pint. Now for the rest of the notices..........

Talking points

- What skills, knowledge and awareness training are needed for visiting the sick or distressed?

- What skills, knowledge, and awareness training are needed for working with the bereaved?
- What skills and training are needed for taking communion to the housebound?
- What kind of person would be right for these ministries? Does anyone come to mind?
- What kind of preparation should be offered to young people and to adults who seek confirmation, and who could offer this preparation?
- What kind of preparation should be offered to parents who want their babies baptised or blessed, and who could offer this preparation?
- What kind of preparation should be offered to couples who come to be married, and who could offer this preparation?
- Are those who greet people and serve refreshments after the service aware of the enormous opportunities in this ministry?

Reflection

One of the biggest dangers faced by any church is that of becoming a club of tightly knit friends. It becomes almost impossible for others to break their way into this group. People who live in the village but do not go to church week by week may gradually feel frozen out and become discouraged from attending at all. Visitors to the community may dread stepping into the church alone, knowing no one and not knowing how to reach out to those inside. The ministry of welcome offered by those who serve refreshments after the service can make all the difference. These are the ministers at the cutting edge of evangelism, outreach and mission. Without such ministries the local church can be as good as dead. Those who are involved in ministries of pastoral care must receive proper training, support and supervision.

Actions

What actions would you want to recommend as a result of your audit on the every member ministries of pastoral care?

24 Ministries of liturgy

Take an audit

There is a range of different ministries which are crucial to the life of the local church. The proper rediscovery of 'every member ministry' exercised by the whole People of God as the Body of Christ is transforming the rural church. For simple analytic purposes this workbook distinguishes between four aspects of every member ministry; characterised here as administration, education, pastoral care and liturgy. All these ministries are of high importance in the local church and require specific gifts, aptitudes, skills and training. Some people may combine ministries across these areas, while other people may prefer to concentrate their energy on one area.

Take an audit of the extent to which lay people are involved in your church in the ministry of liturgy. Think through a normal Sunday service and examine the following questions.

- Are lay people involved in reading lessons?
- Are lay people involved in leading prayers?
- Are lay people involved in distributing communion?
- Are lay people involved in serving at the altar?
- Are lay people involved in leading the service?
- Are lay people involved in other forms of liturgical ministry?

While the Anglican Church is increasingly recognising the proper ministry of lay people in conducting services in a variety of ways, the theology of the church has considered it right to continue to restrict presidency at the eucharist to those ordained to the priesthood. In some rural churches which may have insufficient access to a priest, the practice has grown up of 'communion by extension'. The eucharistic prayer is presided over by a priest in one church and then properly authorised lay ministers take the sacrament from this service for distribution within other satellite congregations.

- Are lay people involved in taking communion by extension in your church?

Bench-marking

The *Rural Churches Survey* assembled information on the extent to which rural churches were supported by lay people being involved in the ministries of liturgy. This aspect of every member ministry was explored through giving particular attention to the following ministries: reading lessons, leading prayers, distributing communion, and serving at the altar. Attention was also given to opportunities for lay ministers to lead the service or to take communion by extension.

Here are the bench-marking statistics for lay participation in the every member ministries of liturgy according to community size.

Table 24: Proportions of churches in which lay people engage in specified ministries of liturgy by community size.

	under 200 %	200-399 %	400-899 %	900 plus %
reading lessons	76	84	91	94
leading prayers	26	31	51	66
distributing communion	26	35	59	70
serving at the altar	16	22	37	55
leading the service	14	24	29	42
taking communion by extension	2	3	2	4

Listening to the statistics

- By far the best established area of lay participation in liturgical ministry is that of lesson reading, which is exercised in 86% of rural churches across the four community sizes.
- Second after lesson reading comes the ministry of distributing communion, which is exercised by lay people in 47% of rural churches across the four community sizes.
- Third in line comes the ministry of leading prayers, which is exercised by lay

people in 41% of rural churches across the four community sizes.

- The ministry of altar server is exercised by lay people in 32% of rural churches across the four community sizes.
- Lay people are involved in the ministry of leading the service in 27% of rural churches across the four community sizes.
- In all these ministries of reading lessons, distributing communion, leading prayers, serving at the altar and leading the service, lay people are more likely to be involved in larger communities than in smaller communities. For example, while lay people share the ministry of reading lessons in 94% of churches in communities of 900 plus, the proportion falls to 76% in communities under 200. While lay people share the ministry of leading services in 42% of churches in communities of 900 plus, the proportion falls to 14% in communities under 200.
- Very little emphasis has been placed on communion by extension within rural churches.
- Across all four community sizes just 3% of churches have developed lay ministry in this direction.

Talking points

- What skills and training are needed for lesson reading, and who could be involved?
- What skills and training are needed for leading prayers, and who could be involved?
- What skills and training are needed for distributing communion, and who could be

involved?

- Is it helpful to develop serving at the altar, and who could be involved?
- Is it helpful to expand the opportunities for lay people to share in leading services, and who should be involved?
- Would communion by extension be helpful in your area or benefice?
- How will the sharing of these ministries make the worship of your church more life-enhancing and attractive to the wider community?

Reflection

The conduct of liturgy and the leadership of services is one of the most public aspects of the church's ministry. Liturgy is capable both of nurturing the faithful and of proclaiming the gospel to enquirers. Churches which offer unprepared or poorly presented liturgy do a grave disservice to their ministry as a whole. Ordained and lay ministers alike need to give proper thought to the way in which their presentation of liturgy is perceived by regular members of the congregation, by less regular attenders and by visitors. Good voice production, care over vestments or clothes, and consideration given to posture and movement should all count very highly. The presentation of a service is not dissimilar from the presentation of a drama.

Actions

What actions would you want to recommend as a result of your audit on the every member ministry of liturgy?

25 Community involvement

Take an audit

It is often suggested that the boundaries between the rural church and the rest of rural life are very porous. If the notion of every member ministry is really taken seriously in the rural church, then it is important to recognise just how far this ministry infiltrates and permeates a great deal of the local community. Just take, for example, a group of people who are already clearly identified with the parish church by virtue of their membership of the Parochial Church Council. How much does this clearly identifiable group of people have contact with other aspects of local life?

Draw up a list of organisations and groups which are based in or linked to the community. Now ask each member of the Parochial Church Council with which of these other organisations or groups he or she is associated. Make sure to include such areas as the Parish Council, the Women's Institute, the Royal British Legion, the Young Farmers Club, the Village Hall Committee, school governors, senior citizens clubs, school parent and teacher associations, sports and recreational clubs, youth organisations and play groups.

Bench-marking

The *Rural Churches Survey* assembled information on the extent to which members of the Parochial Church Council were also involved in other local organisations and groups. If the Parochial Church Council represented more than one church the emphasis was placed in the specific member who represented each individual church included in the survey. The survey specifically referred to the following organisations and groups: the Parish Council, the Women's Institute, the Royal British Legion, the Young Farmers Club, the Village Hall Committee, school governors, senior citizen's clubs, school parent and teachers associations, sports and recreational clubs (including activities like crochet and bowls), youth organisations and play groups.

Here are the bench-marking statistics for the involvement of members of the Parochial Church Council in other areas of local life according to community size.

Table 25: Proportions of churches in which members of the Parochial Church Council are involved in specified organisations and groups by community size.

	under 200 %	200-399 %	400-899 %	900 plus %
Parish Council	62	76	80	65
Women's Institute	52	66	78	74
Village Hall Committee	44	69	76	67
school governors	31	49	75	82
senior citizens' clubs	19	29	45	57
school parent teacher association	15	29	38	47
sports club (for example, bowls)	15	25	36	38
Royal British Legion	14	25	24	35
youth organisation	10	17	23	38
Young Farmers Club	15	17	19	14
play group	10	15	22	26

Listening to the statistics

- There is a very strong overlap between membership of the Parochial Church Council and membership of the Parish Council, with this being the case for 71% of churches across the four community sizes. The overlap is strongest in the middle size communities: 76% in communities between 200 and 399, and 80% in communities between 400 and 899.
- Across the four community sizes two out of every three Parochial Church Councils (67%) share members with the Women's Institute.
- Across all four community sizes, 63% of churches have Parochial Church Council members on the Village Hall Committee.
- Across all four community sizes, 58% of churches have Parochial Church Council members who are also school governors.
- Links with the Royal British Legion are maintained by a quarter (24%) of Parochial Church Council members across all four community sizes.
- Links with the Young Farmers Club are maintained by one in six (16%) of

Parochial Church Council members across all four community sizes.

- Overall the strongest link between the Parochial Church Council and other organisations and groups appear to be in communities of between 400 and 899 inhabitants. These are communities large enough to begin to support a range of groups but small enough to need to save people being committed to several groups.

'That's my PCC badge, that one is my British Legion badge, that is my honorary membership of the W.I and that is my 'Save the Hedgehog' badge'

Talking points

- What difference does it make to the rural church to know that its Parochial Church Council members have links with so many other organisations and groups within the local community?
- What difference could it make to community groups in your parish to know that some of its members are also on the Parochial Church Council?
- How do those Parochial Church Council members who are involved with other community groups use that position and ministry?
- How does your church recognise, pray for, and support its members' ministries in those community groups and other non-church activities?

Reflection

Being a church member in a rural community provides an embodied witness to the faith. People do not remain anonymous for long in small communities, and Christians should not want to hide their faith anyway. In small communities witness and evangelism do not take place effectively by overtly talking about the faith at every opportunity, but by quietly modelling the influence of faith on every aspect of daily life, although there may be occasions when Christian principles will need to be declared.

Actions

What actions would you want to recommend as a result of your audit of the way in which your church is involved in the wider life of the community?

CONCLUSION

Mission Strategy

Introduction

The traditional mission style for the rural church in the Church of England has been 'to be there' for all the people. From that base of being the 'soul of the community' churches have tried to use every chance to heighten awareness of the spiritual realities and the God-given moral commandments. The opportunities of life's great moments, at times of birth, marriage and death, offered further chances to help people place their whole life in the context of eternity. This is still the case. However, secularisation and a pattern of living that offers a large number of distractions, coupled with the loss of connection to one's place of origin, has weakened the tie to Christian continuity which was the foundation for the success of the old parish system.

Currently the prevailing understanding of church is one associated with the evangelical movement. This puts greater emphasis on the church as a distinctive community of faith. In the anonymity of urban areas this understanding of church has a positive contribution to make. In rural areas it can conflict with the older understanding that sees the church as a part of the community, hallowing the whole.

One mark of such a church is in its understanding of membership. Parishes can have a schizophrenic approach to the electoral roll. To have many names on the roll implies an open policy to membership. To reduce the number, perhaps driven by the financial consequences of paying a larger share to the diocese, may sit comfortably with a tighter understanding of membership.

When words like 'membership' and 'fellowship' are more commonly used, they emphasize a sharper divide between those 'of the church' and those who are outside. This is most acutely felt in baptism policy. Many an Anglican will have felt the pain of being pressured to decide whether they can go along with the more clearly expressed statements of commitment to Christ in modern baptism services. In older forms the statement of belief was perhaps vaguer, less clear and more acceptable to those who retain doubts. Clergy need to find the sensitivity to allow people, who enquire about baptism for children or grandchildren, the choice between Thanksgiving after childbirth and full baptism. Such sensitivity is a grace from God.

This is one clear example of the hardening of the line which used to be fuzzier. It was commonplace for those who never attended church still to claim that they were Church of England. We do not know if the decline in the proportion of people claiming such affiliation is a falling away from faith, or if it is in part a result of the Church itself making the demand of commitment clearer. Thus the challenge to share the faith by evangelism is more spoken of at the present time. It is important to understand the difference between evangelism and the broader mission of the Church, in which evangelism is but one tool.

Services and ministry

The service pattern

Faith in the Countryside, the report by the Archbishops' Commission on Rural Areas (1990), argued that, despite the difficulties in finding the leaders for worship, the best strategy for a pattern of worship in a benefice would be for each parish to have a consistent time for its main act of worship. That many benefices design their pattern of worship on the availability of the priest has led a significant number of parishes not to have a weekly act of worship. Table 1 on page 11 shows how nearly half of the communities of under 400 inhabitants did not have an act of worship on the first Sunday in the month. We believe this to be a mistaken strategy. Table 2 on page 15 shows that the practice of midweek services has not ceased. It may be that this worship is in the hands of local lay people, being true to the Christian tradition of public prayer. We would encourage this for it is a reminder to all the people of the main purpose of the church building being there in the first place.

If the intention is to provide worship only for those who come regularly, then the church accepts that it has become a clique, a cult. If the intention is to provide for those who may come, if only seldom, then it is important to recognise that regularity of time is a key factor in helping people over the hurdle of taking that first step across the church's threshold. For this to be able to happen more people must be involved as leaders of worship, more effort must be put into informing the public when the worship takes place, and more care must be taken to ensure that the worship offered relates to the world in which people live.

A growing body of people realise that the church's calendar with special days bears less relation to the annual cycle of the world in which we try to present the Gospel. It may be as important to develop a special act of worship which forms part of the cricket festival or the summer village fete as to commemorate the anniversary of the church's dedication. It is not difficult to identify monthly secular occasions that might lend themselves to an appropriate act of worship to which people are specially invited.

A further consequence of shaping the liturgical pattern round the needs of the clergy is the development of 'united' services across the benefice. In most cases this results in a happy occasion for those who are willing to travel, but that number is nearly always a reduction on the total that would have been at worship had each church maintained its own service. While there are benefits to be had from parishes cooperating across the benefice, there are also losses which should not be ignored. Some benefices now hold their united service in mid-week, as an extra to the Sunday pattern, so as not to disturb the loyalty to the local which is so strong in rural areas. Not to have a service in a parish each week is to break the link with the community and to emphasize that the church has moved from belonging to that community to becoming a special community on its own.

The range of spirituality and personality type suggests that the church should provide a range of worship styles. The experience though is that the choice of worship types has been severely reduced in recent years. An example is the reduction in frequency or cessation of the quieter early morning holy communion service. People are unlikely to accept a one-style-fits-all approach to worship. How to respond to the range of spiritualities remains a challenge to the church at large.

The role of the clergy

The continuing decline in the numbers of full-time stipendiary parochial clergy has been more than matched by a growth in the numbers of readers, that uniquely Anglican order of ministry, and, for the time being, a growth in the number of retired clergy. Probably even more important is the growth of new forms of lay ministry such as pastors and worship leaders, who may, with clergy and readers, be called a local ministry team.

As the statistics show, the smaller settlements have not been able to jettison their reliance on clergy as much as have the larger places. It is clear that the role of the stipendiary clergy has been changing from the one who does everything in ministerial terms to the one who makes sure that everything is done by someone. This suggests that in some cases a benefice needs a manager as much as it needs a priestly, holy person. Further, a benefice with numerous parishes has to decide whether it wants its priest to be such a manager or to be the person who leads the spiritual life of the several churches, and what skills are needed to make sure necessary administration is well done.

We note that, as stipendiary clergy diminish in number, there are moves in secular authorities to appoint local patch workers for the purpose of community development. We regret that the church may have been so concerned with its own survival that the opportunities to work in partnership with other bodies seeking to serve the rural areas have been largely ignored. These opportunities can be revisited by discussing the social benefits of the church's work with those whose interests overlap with the church's own.

We wish to question the assumption that the vicar should live in the largest settlement (see table 3). If we are to adapt to the reality that the stipendiary priest is to be an enabler of the ministry of others, then it could be more appropriate for the parsonage not to be in the busiest place where more public demands will come to the door of the priest. The assumption which places the parsonage in the busiest place carries with it the assumption that most of the ministry is still in the hands of the stipendiary clergy. It also carries an assumption that smaller places are less important than larger ones. We do not agree with these assumptions.

Local community

So often one hears the complaint from places within even 100 miles of a city that the old rural lifestyle has been replaced with urban values brought by the increasing number of commuters. It is true that farming occupies a diminishing number of people, a process that has been taking place steadily over 150 years, to the point that other occupations, particularly in tourism, provide a larger share of rural Gross Domestic Product than agriculture. The use of the internet makes it possible for many businesses to be run from homes. In rural areas a greater part of the workforce is employed in micro-companies with fewer than ten people than is the case in urban areas.

The replacement of public transport by private cars, and the withdrawal of the amenities that might be deemed necessary for a place to be described as self-sufficient, are both consequence and contributor to the choice for individual freedom to live and move at one's own pleasure. Even in our small, wealthy and well-populated country, there are pressures to contain the cost of delivering services, like post office, utilities, shops and health, to the more thinly populated areas.

The church is not immune to these economic realities. Redistribution of the church's assets, finance and clergy, for the benefit of urban areas has been largely at the expense of the rural church in modern times. In many rural dioceses which used perhaps to be resource rich in the past, parishes are required to find the whole cost of having a paid cleric, and these costs include training and pension as well as current salary.

We note that high rural house prices are changing the composition of many rural settlements. We should be asking what it is that makes people buy a house in a rural area. Might they be looking for privacy? If so, then the use they may wish to make of the church may be different from those more extravert individuals who are committed to people doing things together. Is the emphasis on 'family services' and overt friendliness perhaps unappealing to some? On the other hand, newcomers may be searching for the ideal community in which to belong and play a part; the local church can help them fulfil this dream.

Schools

The incoming Labour Government of 1997 put a stop to the closure of schools on the grounds of size alone. Rural communities value their local primary school. It gives hope that those looking to move into their area will be young families on which so much community life depends. But children do not remain forever young, and a total population of around 2000 is possibly needed to produce a sufficient and consistent supply of children to create a large enough primary school population.

The links between church and school are important for both institutions. Whether the school be a church school or not, the staff are important contributors to the overall well-being of the community, including cleaners, assistants and governors, as well as teachers. The church for its part must work with the staff to affirm their vocation, for the adult citizens of tomorrow have the adults they meet when they are children as their models. The curriculum does not allow for proselytisation, but the relationships that are possible during out-of-curriculum activities can develop a child's understanding of the life of faith and the contribution the church can make to the whole of life.

Young people

When children become teenagers the way they are perceived by adults may also change. Teenagers may be felt to be a threat. One result is that conversations between adults and teenagers are tense. Yet teenagers are exploring the adult world and coping with inner and external confusions. Teenagers may have a brusque way of asking the important questions, and may have undeveloped finesse in giving an opinion. Adults need to remember that young people are testing out our boundaries and our understandings; maybe that is why we find them a threat for our own uncertainties are exposed. Our workbook *Rural Youth*, published by ACORA in 2001, shows how the views of young people on life's big questions develop. That workbook offers material for opening up conversations with young people and taking their own development seriously.

Church work with teenagers is a challenge for smaller communities, but the relationship between caring adults and even a handful of local young people will at least leave a memory that 'they cared'. Across a benefice of several parishes or the deanery it is possible to mount a substantial youth project. If the local authority is willing to be involved, then what may begin as a church project can become an important contribution to the well-being of many young people. Such church work must be done in the name of all denominations and should not exclude any young people on faith grounds.

Amenities

The Parish Council has the main responsibility to work for the maintenance of those necessary amenities which contribute to a sustainable community. Cooperative action is fundamental, and the church should show its interest in the work of the Parish Council. A substantial proportion of Parochial Church Councils have at least one member on the Parish Council and it is expected that this person has a duty to represent in both directions. Religion and politics are two sides of the same coin - life on earth. If religion has no connection with politics it is emasculated; if politics has no connection with religion it is demoralised. The local church may be able to allocate land or buildings to allow for the provision of some important amenity. Often an ancient charity with unused resources is under the control of 'vicar and churchwardens'.

Bridging the Gap, published by ACORA in 1999, develops the theme of the relationship between the church and the local community. Its authors, experienced in community development work, explore ways for local churches to work in partnership with those organisations that share a concern for the well being of rural people.

Other churches

Our Christian partners in other denominations have also experienced cut backs in resources and the availability of ministers. Ecumenical cooperation is too often experienced as drudgery and thus it has insufficient enthusiastic support. Each denomination has been doing resource planning in isolation. Thus it may now be too late to prevent significant areas of countryside being without a full-time paid cleric of any denomination. If only the different traditions of Christendom had seen the writing on the wall much earlier we might have been more willing to share resources, buildings and ministry. We welcome the small areas of experiment in joint planning and urge that this should happen across larger areas.

The Churches Rural Group of Churches Together in England has addressed the difficulty for Christians who may find that their parent denomination has no place of worship within easy reach. Every mainstream denomination in England has now adopted a policy of ecumenical hospitality, designed for places where there is only one church, which is increasingly the case in rural areas. This has the effect of inviting all Christians to consider the local church as open to them without losing allegiance to their parent denomination. Such a policy has to be formally adopted by the local church before it can apply.

Church Life

Pattern of church attendance

Counting heads is a complicated process which exercises churchwardens and statisticians. We certainly need a better understanding of the pattern of church attendance to advise whether or not a reduction in the opportunities for public worship is damaging the mission of the Church. It would also be useful to explore the impact of less traditional ways and places of worshipping. Some suggest that worship outside attracts more attenders; that worship in a building that has other non-ecclesiastical uses, such as a village hall or school, is more popular than in the parish church. There are many accounts of a very significant proportion of a village population attending church over the Christmas period if there is a range of worship opportunities (see table 12). It is even possible that the smaller the community, the greater is the proportion of the people who attend church at Christmastime.

The less prescriptive approach to liturgy employed in *Common Worship* offers a challenge to those who put little effort into the design and delivery of worship. There should be more sharing of good experiences and a greater requirement on clergy to take advantage of in-service training in liturgical innovation.

Church activities

The parish magazine could be the greatest contribution to the church's mission. It exists as much in the smaller as the larger communities (see table 14). More research is needed to explore its contribution. It would have an even greater potential if it were to be recognised and made use of by many authorities who envy the church its local connectedness.

The church building

Not all our smallest communities have public meeting places, like a pub or a village hall. Quite often the church is the only place in which community activities can take place. This use could be more comfortable and frequent if the building were adapted to allow for it. Some churches are not able to be adapted, but most could be if there were willingness and funds to cover the cost. To adapt a church to provide toilets, heating, kitchens and meeting spaces costs about 20-25% of the cost of building a new village hall.

A postal survey of all rural deans, carried out by Jeremy Martineau in 2000, shows that of all Church of England churches serving communities under 3,000 population, half are in use for a wide range of community activities. These may extend from play groups to polling stations, lunch clubs for the elderly to drop-in centres for the young; even post offices, shops and farmers markets can be found taking place in churches. The most common use is for arts and music events. Not every small community has frequent need for a community hall, although it should be noted that perhaps the old vicarage once used to be a place where community events took place. Its sale may thus have removed more than a dwelling for a parson. The adaptation of part of the church as a facility for such occasional use can be a real blessing and is a reminder to all that God is a God of all aspects of life. *Open All Hours,* published by ACORA in 2001, shares experience and advice on how such adaptations can best be brought about.

In a large benefice it may be that the different church buildings can focus on a particular use. One might be a place of prayer and meditation for people from far and wide. Another might be more easily adapted for work with the young, and another as a place for artistic expression. Many churches are of potential interest to visitors. The ministry to visitors is being developed in increasing numbers of churches. Our *Rural Visitors* workbook, published by ACORA in 2001, shows how to do this and what visitors actually want from such a visit.

Every member ministry

British society has become less hierarchical and much more participative in many areas. From filling your own car with fuel to DIY the servant class has to a large extent been replaced with a middle class that cannot afford domestic help, even though both adult partners may be in paid employment. On one hand, therefore, there is a greater willingness to 'have a go' at something new, but there may be less time available to do so. Compound this with an uncertainty about some aspects of life, like law, medicine and religion, and there is continuing confusion about whether it is safe for 'lay people' to do things that were previously wrapped in mystery and thus the preserve of the 'initiated and authorised professionals', who, in the case of the church, are the clergy.

In rural areas the newcomers may have brought an education and professionalism of their own. They may not so readily assume that the clergy are the only ones who are capable of bearing the responsibilities of ministry. First, untrained lay people read scripture, then led prayers, assisted with the distribution of the sacrament, even gave testimony and led non-eucharistic worship. As our workbook *Rural Ministry*, published by ACORA in 1999, shows the tide towards liturgical leadership being widely shared has gone far, but is still resisted by some. As one bishop has said, 'I would rather than have lay people officiating at the altar than preaching from the pulpit'. Need and opportunity have gone hand in hand to change a number of features of church life, but such changes do not yet permit lay presidency at the eucharist. Interestingly the Free Churches likewise generally baulk at this step-too-far.

In matters pastoral, however, there is no such constraint. Good neighbourliness can be developed into well qualified counselling for the bereaved, training for couples planning marriage, and visiting the sick and housebound. As society has developed a generation of trained counsellors these skills are more widely available to the local church, and should be well used with appropriate professional supervision.

Thus the hands-on work of the clergy is now very widely shared. In the situation of having numerous separate churches under their care the stipendiary clergy are developing new skills as trainers, supervisors, teachers of theology and are sometimes described as 'bishops-in-little'. This changed role needs to be understood by the public at large as well as by church people and not least by the clergy themselves.

This offers an enlarged opportunity to play an important part in the development of a holistic approach to a better society for all. Professionals in health trusts, social services departments, the criminal justice system and even economic development departments of local authorities still look with respect to the local knowledge that is assumed of the clergy. There is little cohesion between the various professions and there is opportunity for clergy to assume a humble role in bringing together the other professionals in the common cause of this 'better society'.

Lay people have a life beyond the walls of the church. There is a huge reservoir of competence, interest, professionalism spanning the whole of life. If the church were to mount a mission strategy based on the skills of the lay people, the church would take off in new directions, perhaps with more likelihood of being listened to with respect and interest. To begin with, each church should conduct a skills audit of its regular attenders. This information could be pooled across the deanery to see what course of action might emerge. If new ways of being church are to be developed one piece of the new pattern will surely be special interest groups. An example of this was the ability of the rural Church to respond to the Foot and Mouth outbreak in such an exemplary way. Over 200 Christian volunteers with agricultural knowledge formed area groups under the Farm Crisis Network (a project of the Agricultural Christian Fellowship and the Arthur Rank Centre). These groups have been working supportively with hundreds of farming families whose lives were damaged by the disease in 2001. This work continues.

Faith in the future

As the local church responds to these various pressures and opportunities, it will need visionary and empowering leadership at diocesan level. The church must seek to reconnect with its local community and the shared concerns. The church should not hold back from sharing its Christian insights for the benefit of all the people. Likewise, as the local church works out what the faith means in its own life, it should be bold enough to see that it is the visible struggling with the questions of faith that will give it credibility, rather than wait until all the answers are clear.

We believe that the people of these islands are not waiting to be convinced by something spectacular, but are keen to be invited to share in the search for meaning which is the nature of true discipleship. As the ministry is shared, so others will come to see that the life of faith is one for them too. As the church building is used in ways that are recognizably useful for the community new connections will be made with those for whom God is not just a distant idea, but an ever-present reality. As the worship explores new ways of praising and praying others will come to see that 'being in church' is to be in a place of adventure. As Christian people learn to share their search for God then others will see that the Christian life is for them too.

Be bold. Pray for God's guidance. Try new things, even if they seem to have been tried before. Be willing to share your own questions and your tentative answers. Do not be embarrassed if only two or three come together. Invite young people to help you make sense of the big questions. Organize worship in places other than the church building.